11+

NON-VERBAL REASONING

Standard Short Tests

Testbook 1

Stephen C. Curran
and
Andrea Richardson

edited by Dr. Tandip Mann

This book belongs to:

....

Accelerated Education Publications Ltd

Non-verbal Reasoning Test 1

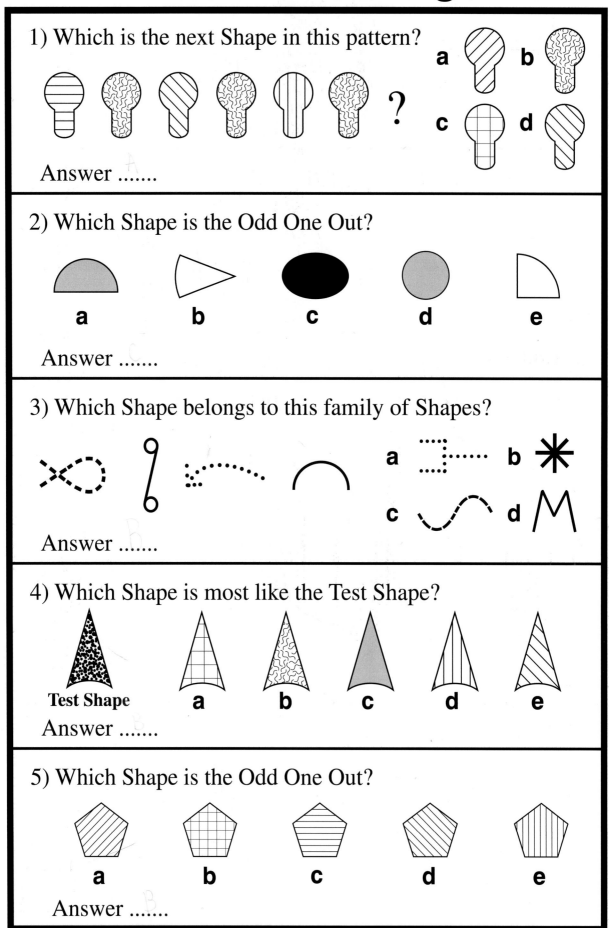

1) Which is the next Shape in this pattern?

a   b

c   d

?

Answer ....

2) Which Shape is the Odd One Out?

a   b   c   d   e

Answer ....

3) Which Shape belongs to this family of Shapes?

a   b

c   d

Answer ....

4) Which Shape is most like the Test Shape?

Test Shape   a   b   c   d   e

Answer ....

5) Which Shape is the Odd One Out?

a   b   c   d   e

Answer ....

© 2010 Stephen Curran

6) Which Shape does not fit in with the others?

a	b	c	d	e

Answer ....

7) Which Figure belongs to this collection of Figures?

a b c d

Answer ....

8) Which Shape does not fit in with the others?

a	b	c	d	e

Answer ....

9) Which is the next Shape in this pattern?

?

a b c d

Answer ....

10) Which Shape does not fit in with the others?

a	b	c	d	e

Answer ....

Score

ae © 2010 Stephen Curran

3

Non-verbal Reasoning Test 2

1) Which is the next Shape in this pattern?

a   b

c   d

Answer ....

2) Which Shape does not fit in with the others?

a   b   c   d   e

Answer ....

3) Which is the next Shape in this Series?

?

a   b

c   d

Answer ....

4) Which Shape is most like the Test Shape?

Test Shape   a   b   c   d   e

Answer ....

5) Which Shape is the Odd One Out?

a   b   c   d   e

Answer ....

© 2010 Stephen Curran

6) Which Shape is the Odd One Out?

a   b   c   d   e

Answer ....

7) Which Shape belongs to this family of Shapes?

T V F W D

a   b   c   d

Answer ....

8) Which Shape is the Odd One Out?

a   b   c   d   e

Answer ....

9) Which is the next Shape in this Series?

?   a   b   c   d

Answer ....

10) Which Shape is the Odd One Out?

a   b   c   d   e

Answer ....

Score

ae © 2010 Stephen Curran

Non-verbal Reasoning Test 3

1) Which is the next Shape in this pattern?

a   b   c   d

Answer ....

2) Which Shape is the Odd One Out?

a   b   c   d   e

Answer ....

3) Which Shape belongs to this family of Shapes?

F   ∿   ⊥   X   a O   b S   c y   d <

Answer ....

4) Which Shape is most like the Test Shape?

Test Shape   a   b   c   d   e

Answer ....

5) Which Shape is the Odd One Out?

a   b   c   d   e

Answer ....

© 2010 Stephen Curran

6) Which Shape does not fit in with the others?

a   b   c   d   e

Answer ....

7) Which is the next Shape in this Series?

?

a ■·········· b

c □·········· d ··········□

Answer ....

8) Which two Shapes are most alike?

a   b   c   d   e

Answer .... and ....

9) Which is the next Shape in this Series?

?

a   b

c   d

Answer ....

10) Which Shape is most like the Test Shape?

✕   <   +   ✳   \\\\\\   ,

Test Shape   a   b   c   d   e

Answer ....

Score

ae © 2010 Stephen Curran

Non-verbal Reasoning Test 4

1) Which is the next Shape in this Series?

    ?   **a** 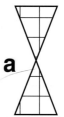 **b** **c** **d**

Answer ....

2) Which Shape does not fit in with the others?

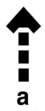      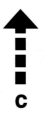      

   a   **b**   **c**   **d**   **e**

Answer ....

3) Which Shape belongs to this family of Shapes?

 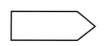   **a** **b**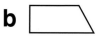

                                     c   **d**

Answer ....

4) Which Shape is most like the Test Shape?

Test Shape   **a**   **b**   **c**   **d**   **e**

Answer ....

5) Which is the next Shape in this Series?

  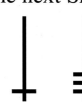    **?**   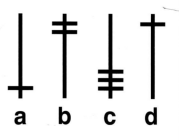

                                             a   **b**   **c**   **d**

Answer ....

© 2010 Stephen Curran

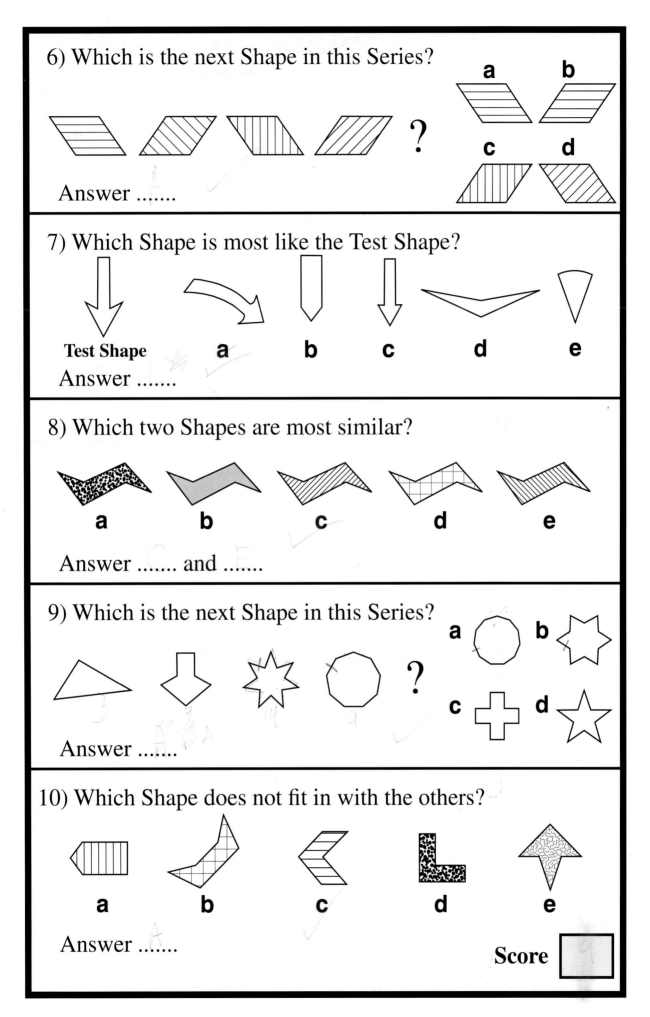

6) Which is the next Shape in this Series?

a   b

c   d

Answer ....

7) Which Shape is most like the Test Shape?

Test Shape   a   b   c   d   e

Answer ....

8) Which two Shapes are most similar?

a   b   c   d   e

Answer .... and ....

9) Which is the next Shape in this Series?

a   b

c   d

Answer ....

10) Which Shape does not fit in with the others?

a   b   c   d   e

Answer ....

Score

ae © 2010 Stephen Curran

Non-verbal Reasoning Test 5

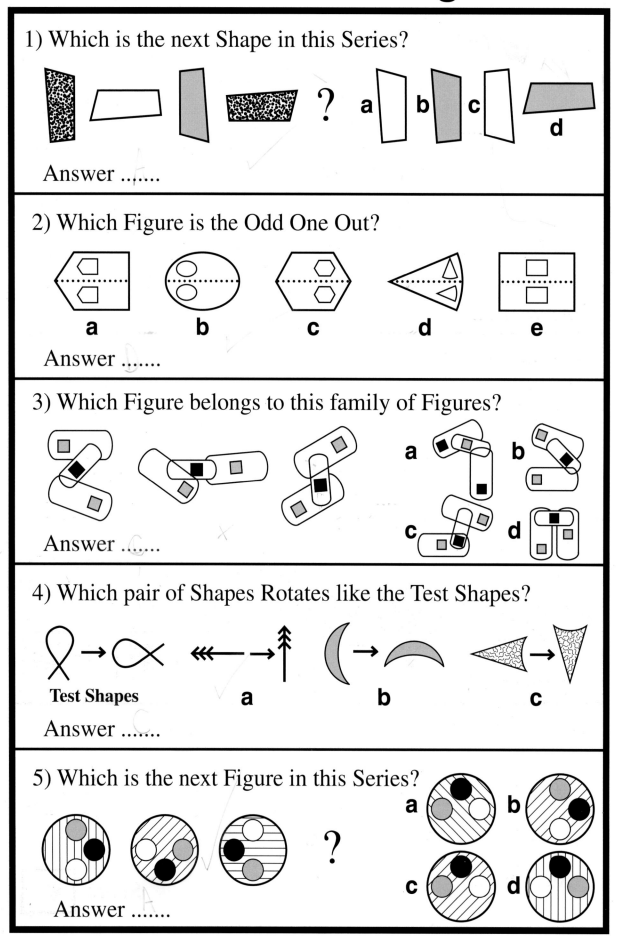

1) Which is the next Shape in this Series?

Answer ....

2) Which Figure is the Odd One Out?

Answer ....

3) Which Figure belongs to this family of Figures?

Answer ....

4) Which pair of Shapes Rotates like the Test Shapes?

Test Shapes

Answer ....

5) Which is the next Figure in this Series?

Answer ....

   © 2010 Stephen Curran

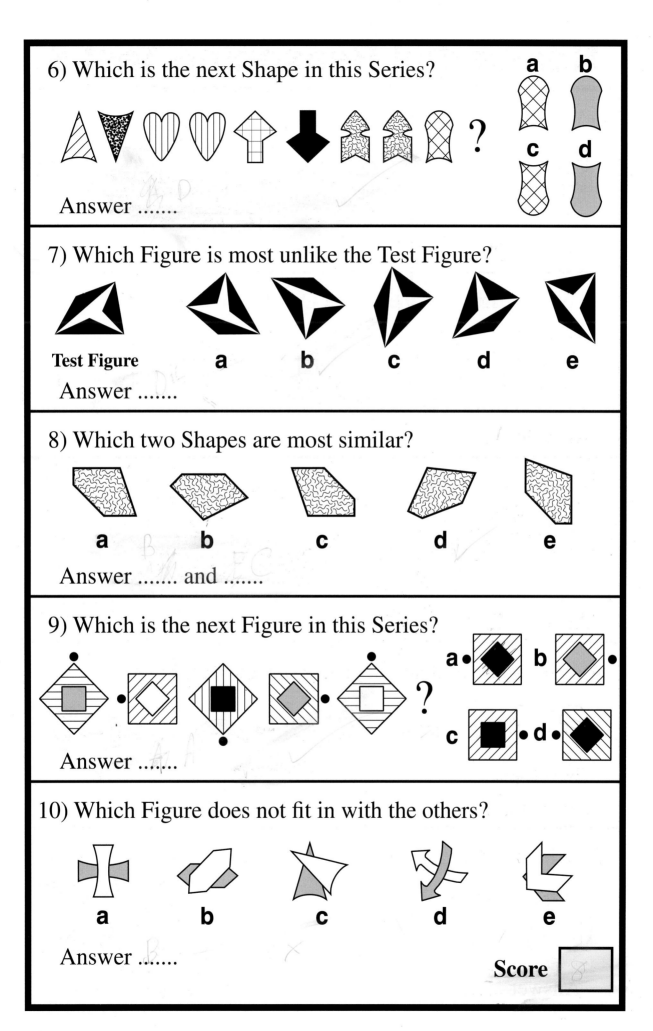

6) Which is the next Shape in this Series?

a b c d

Answer ....

7) Which Figure is most unlike the Test Figure?

Test Figure   a   b   c   d   e

Answer ....

8) Which two Shapes are most similar?

a   b   c   d   e

Answer .... and ....

9) Which is the next Figure in this Series?

a b c d

Answer ....

10) Which Figure does not fit in with the others?

a   b   c   d   e

Answer ....

Score

ae © 2010 Stephen Curran

Non-verbal Reasoning Test 6

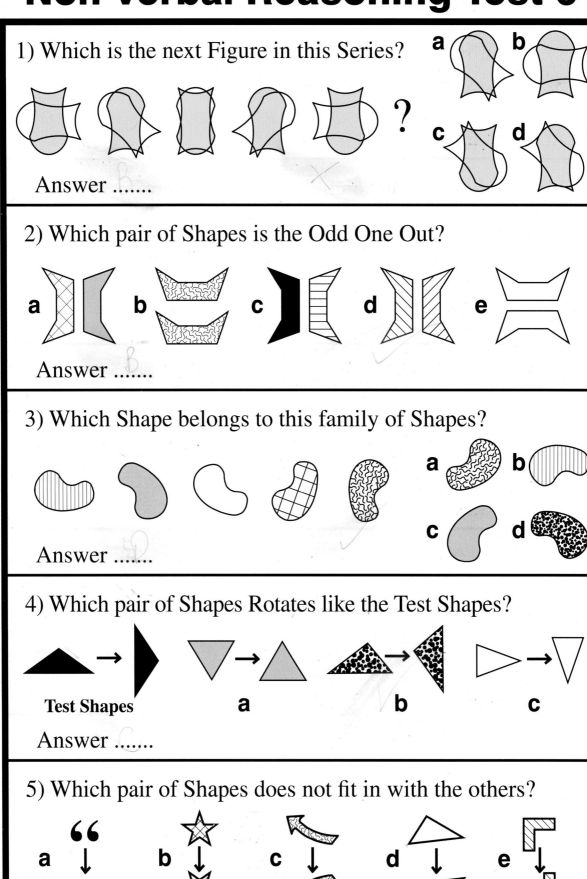

1) Which is the next Figure in this Series?

a   b

c   d

Answer ....

2) Which pair of Shapes is the Odd One Out?

a   b   c   d   e

Answer ....

3) Which Shape belongs to this family of Shapes?

a   b

c   d

Answer ....

4) Which pair of Shapes Rotates like the Test Shapes?

Test Shapes   a   b   c

Answer ....

5) Which pair of Shapes does not fit in with the others?

a   b   c   d   e

Answer ....

© 2010 Stephen Curran

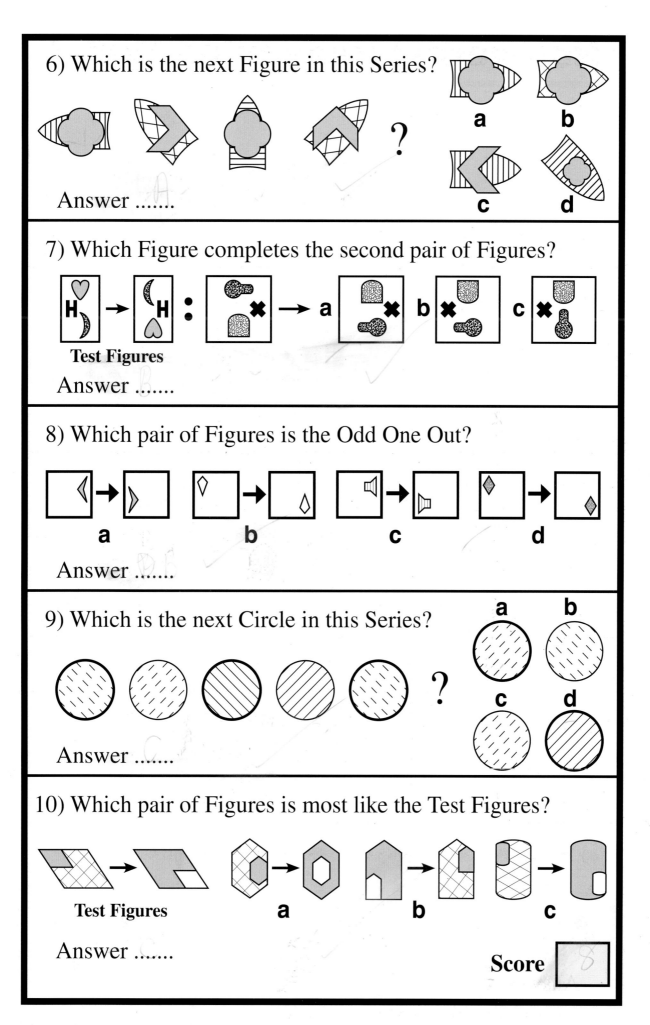

6) Which is the next Figure in this Series?

Answer ....

a b c d

7) Which Figure completes the second pair of Figures?

Test Figures

Answer ....

8) Which pair of Figures is the Odd One Out?

a b c d

Answer ....

9) Which is the next Circle in this Series?

a b c d

Answer ....

10) Which pair of Figures is most like the Test Figures?

Test Figures a b c

Answer ....

Score

ae © 2010 Stephen Curran

Non-verbal Reasoning Test 7

1) Which pair of Shapes Rotates like the Test Shapes?

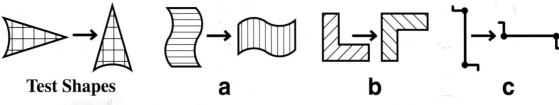

Test Shapes   a   b   c

Answer ....

2) Which Shape is the Odd One Out?

a   b   c   d   e

Answer ....

3) Which Figure belongs to this family of Figures?

Answer ....

4) Which Figure is most like the Test Figure?

Test Figure   a   b   c   d

Answer ....

5) Which pair of Shapes does not fit in with the others?

a   b   c   d   e

Answer ....

      © 2010 Stephen Curran

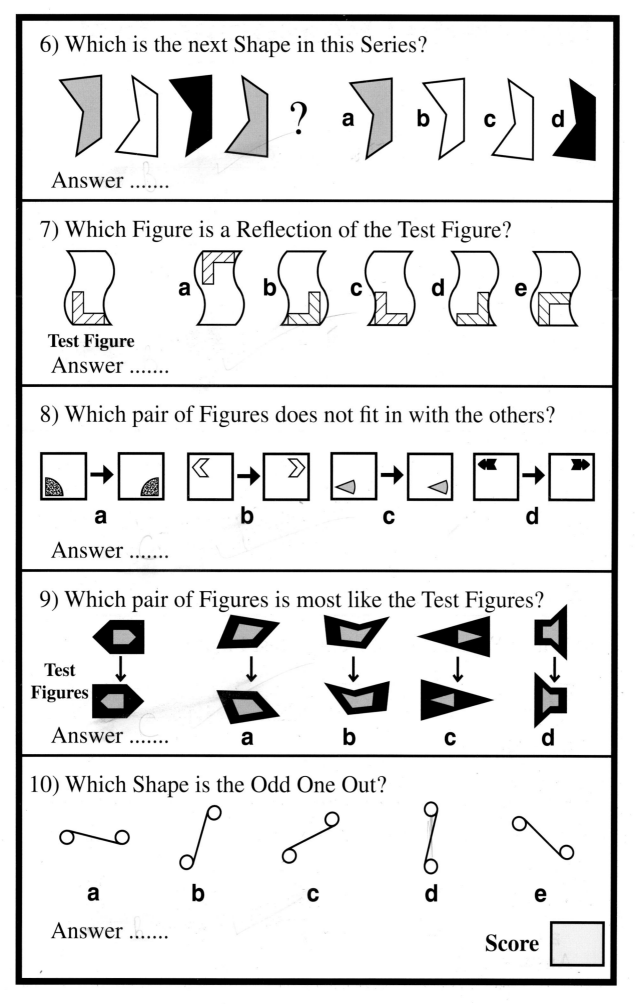

6) Which is the next Shape in this Series?

?   a   b   c   d

Answer ....

7) Which Figure is a Reflection of the Test Figure?

a   b   c   d   e

Test Figure

Answer ....

8) Which pair of Figures does not fit in with the others?

a   b   c   d

Answer ....

9) Which pair of Figures is most like the Test Figures?

Test Figures

Answer ....   a   b   c   d

10) Which Shape is the Odd One Out?

a   b   c   d   e

Answer ....

Score

ae © 2010 Stephen Curran

Non-verbal Reasoning Test 8

1) Which is the next pair of Shapes in this Series?

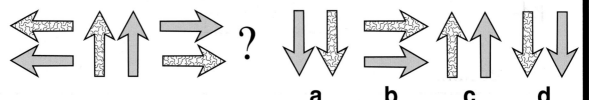

Answer ....

2) Which Shape does not fit in with the others?

   a   **b**   **c**   **d**   **e**

Answer ....

3) Which Shape belongs to this family of Shapes?

W Y A B D E F   a **H**   b **Z**

                                     c **X**   d **C**

Answer ....

4) Which Figure is most like the Test Figure?

Test Figure   **a**   **b**   **c**   **d**

Answer ....

5) Which Figure is the Odd One Out?

   a   **b**   **c**   **d**   **e**

Answer ....

© 2010 Stephen Curran ae

6) Which is the next Shape in this Series?

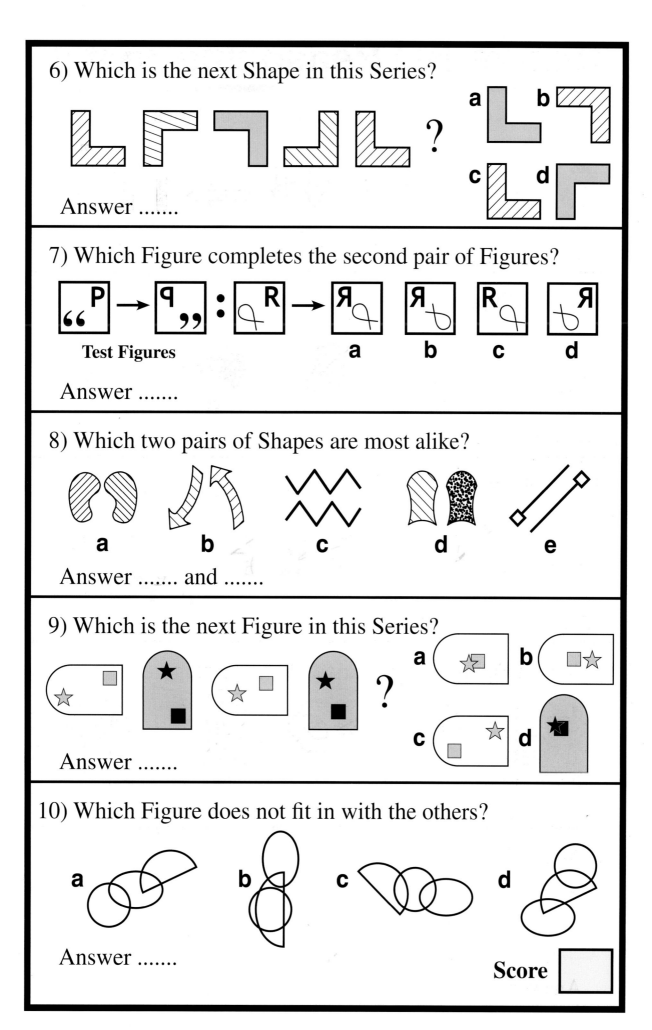

Answer ....

7) Which Figure completes the second pair of Figures?

Test Figures

a   b   c   d

Answer ....

8) Which two pairs of Shapes are most alike?

a   b   c   d   e

Answer .... and ....

9) Which is the next Figure in this Series?

a   b

c   d

Answer ....

10) Which Figure does not fit in with the others?

a   b   c   d

Answer ....

Score

ae © 2010 Stephen Curran

Non-verbal Reasoning Test 9

1) Which is the next Shape in this Series?

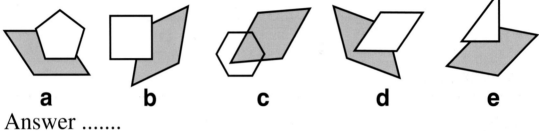

Answer ....

2) Which Figure does not fit in with the others?

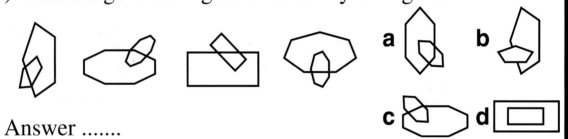

Answer ....

3) Which Figure belongs to this family of Figures?

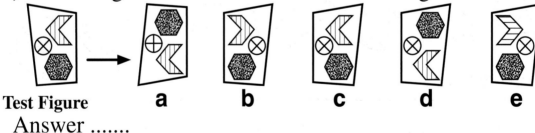

Answer ....

4) Which Figure is a Reflection of the Test Figure?

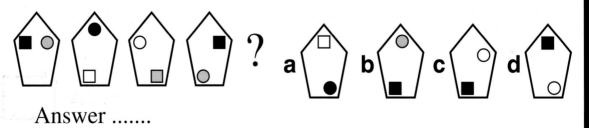

Test Figure

Answer ....

5) Which is the next Figure in this Series?

Answer ....

© 2010 Stephen Curran

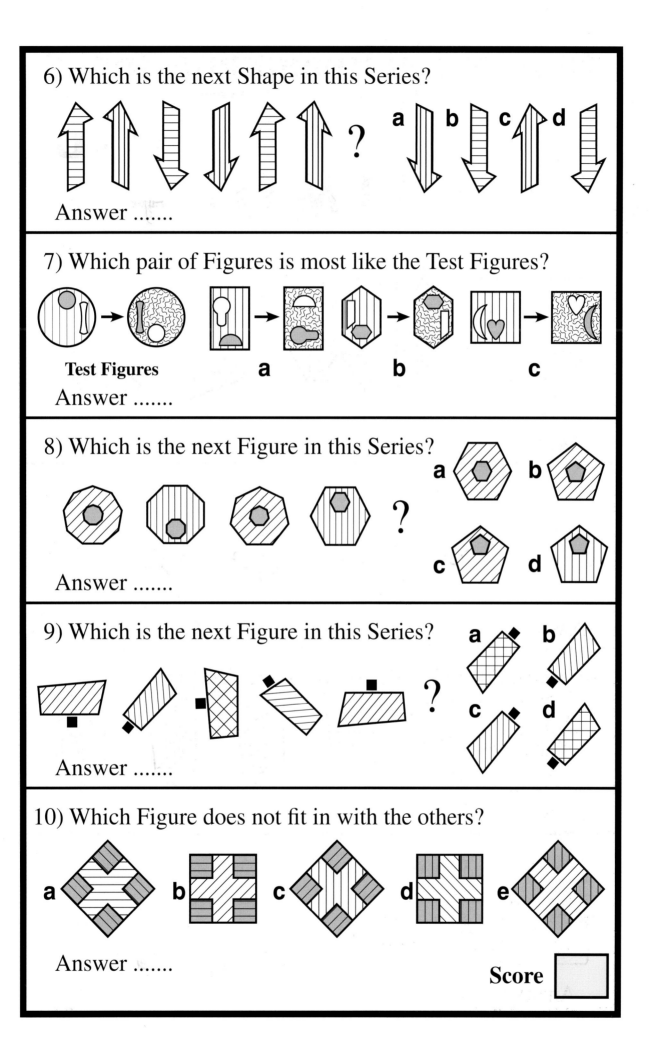

6) Which is the next Shape in this Series?

a b c d

Answer ....

7) Which pair of Figures is most like the Test Figures?

Test Figures   a   b   c

Answer ....

8) Which is the next Figure in this Series?

a   b

?

c   d

Answer ....

9) Which is the next Figure in this Series?

a   b

?

c   d

Answer ....

10) Which Figure does not fit in with the others?

a   b   c   d   e

Answer ....

Score

ae © 2010 Stephen Curran

Non-verbal Reasoning Test 10

1) Which is the next Figure in this Series?

a   b

c   d

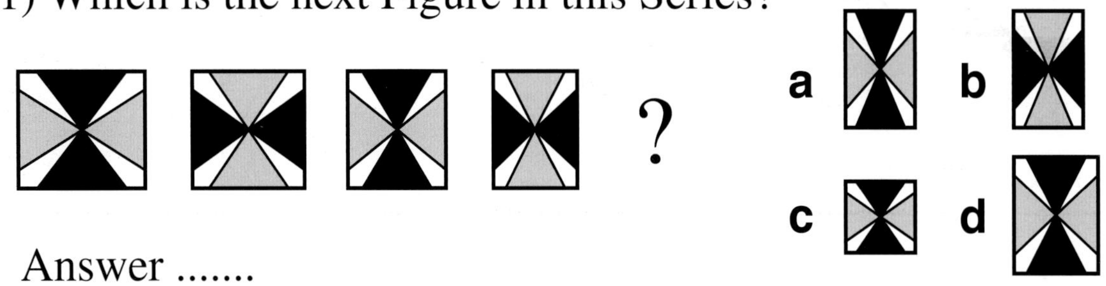

Answer ....

2) Which Figure is the Odd One Out?

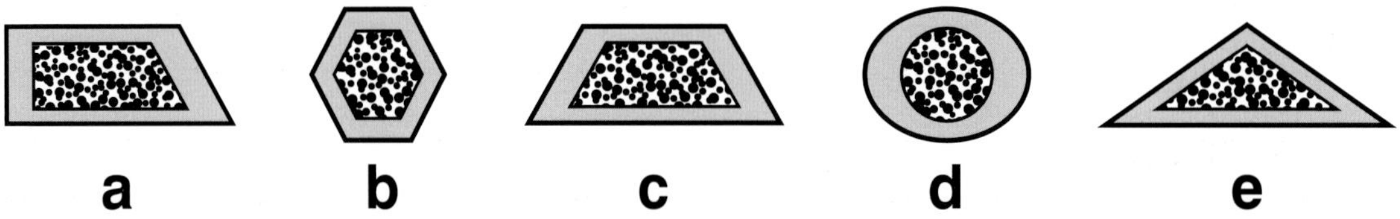

a   b   c   d   e

Answer ....

3) Which pair of Figures belongs to this family of Figures?

E→   X→

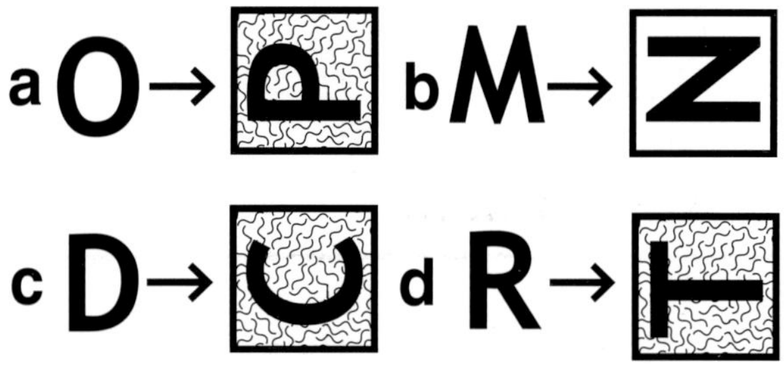

a O→   b M→

c D→   d R→

Answer ....

4) Which pair of Figures is most like the Test Figures?

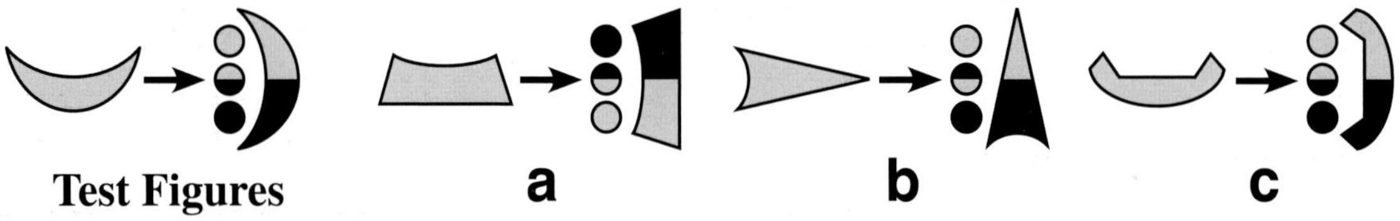

Test Figures   a   b   c

Answer ....

5) Which is the next Figure in this Series?

a   b

c   d

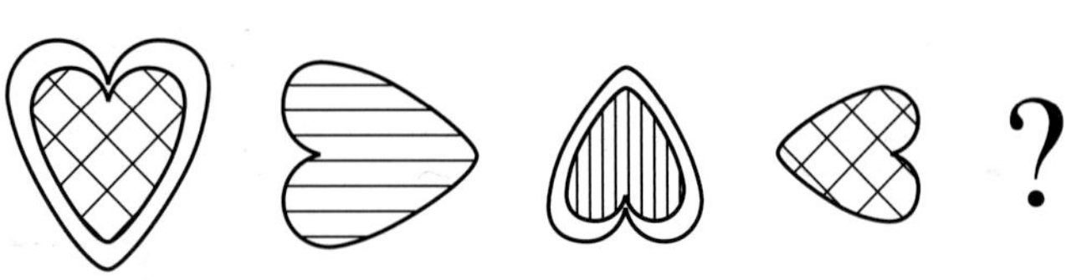

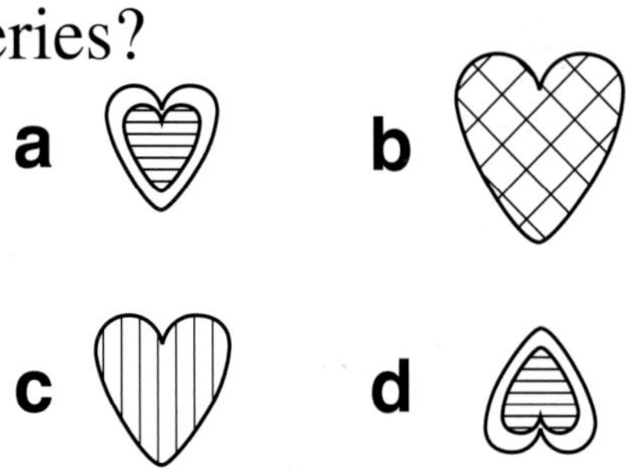

Answer ....

        © 2010 Stephen Curran

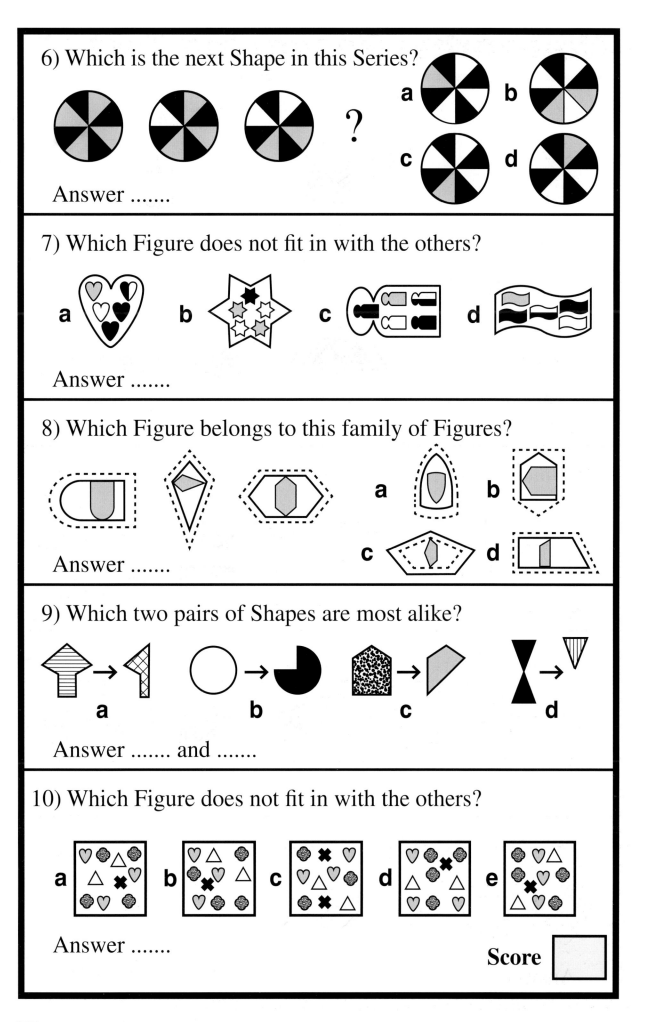

6) Which is the next Shape in this Series?

a   b   c   d

Answer ....

7) Which Figure does not fit in with the others?

a   b   c   d

Answer ....

8) Which Figure belongs to this family of Figures?

a   b   c   d

Answer ....

9) Which two pairs of Shapes are most alike?

a   b   c   d

Answer .... and ....

10) Which Figure does not fit in with the others?

a   b   c   d   e

Answer ....

Score

ae © 2010 Stephen Curran

Non-verbal Reasoning Test 11

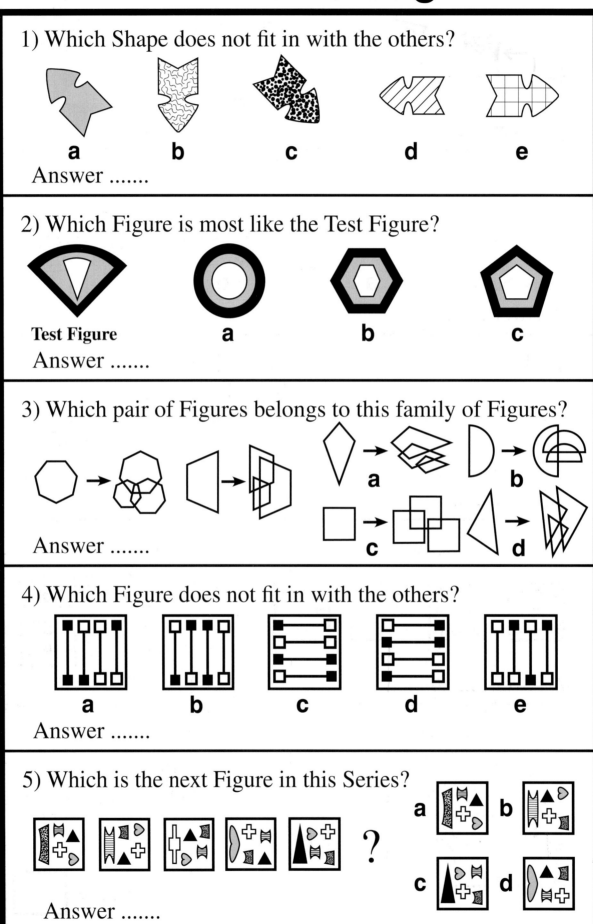

1) Which Shape does not fit in with the others?

a   b   c   d   e

Answer ....

2) Which Figure is most like the Test Figure?

Test Figure   a   b   c

Answer ....

3) Which pair of Figures belongs to this family of Figures?

a   b   c   d

Answer ....

4) Which Figure does not fit in with the others?

a   b   c   d   e

Answer ....

5) Which is the next Figure in this Series?

?   a   b   c   d

Answer ....

    © 2010 Stephen Curran ae

6) Which pair of Figures does not fit in with the others?

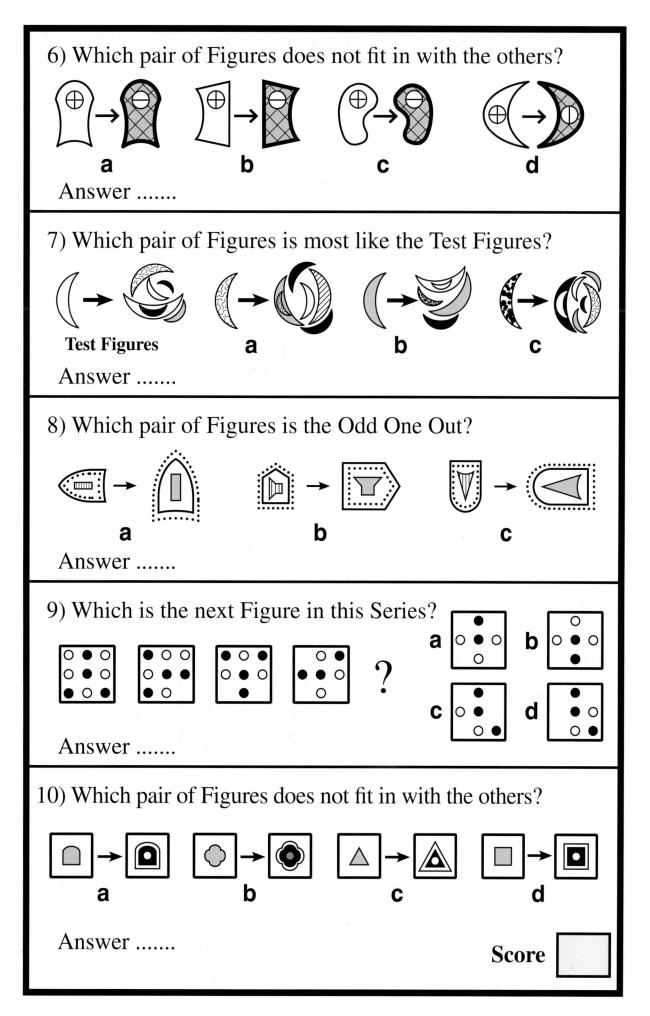

a   b   c   d

Answer ....

7) Which pair of Figures is most like the Test Figures?

Test Figures   a   b   c

Answer ....

8) Which pair of Figures is the Odd One Out?

a   b   c

Answer ....

9) Which is the next Figure in this Series?

?   a   b
          c   d

Answer ....

10) Which pair of Figures does not fit in with the others?

a   b   c   d

Answer ....

Score

ae © 2010 Stephen Curran

Non-verbal Reasoning Test 12

1) Which is the next Figure in this Series?

     ?

a **b**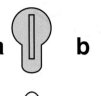

c **d**

Answer ....

2) Which pair of Figures is the Odd One Out?

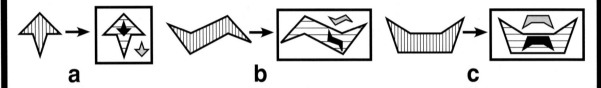

a   **b**   **c**

Answer ....

3) Which Figure belongs to this family of Figures?

  a **b**  **c**

Answer ....

4) Which pair of Figures belongs to this family of Figures?

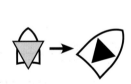

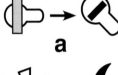 **a** 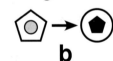 **b**

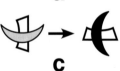 **c** 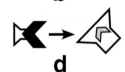 **d**

Answer ....

5) Which is the next Figure in this Series?

   ?

a 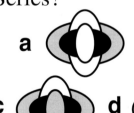 **b**

c 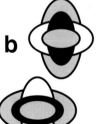 **d**

Answer ....

© 2010 Stephen Curran

6) Which pair of Figures is the Odd One Out?

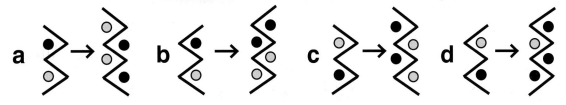

Answer ....

7) Which pair of Figures is most like the Test Figures?

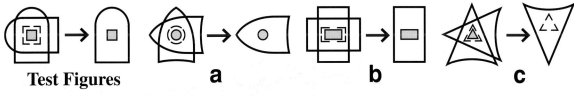

Test Figures

Answer ....

8) Which two Figures are most alike?

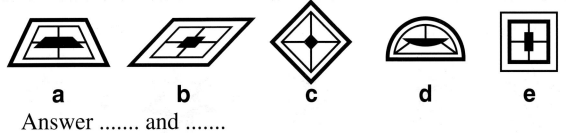

Answer .... and ....

9) Which Figure is next in this Series?

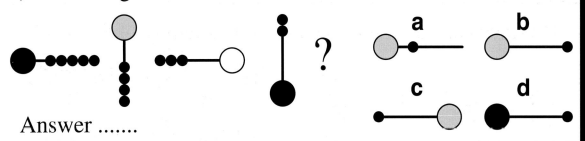

Answer ....

10) Which pair of Figures does not fit in with the others?

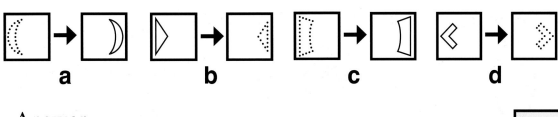

Answer ....

Score

ae © 2010 Stephen Curran

Non-verbal Reasoning Test 13

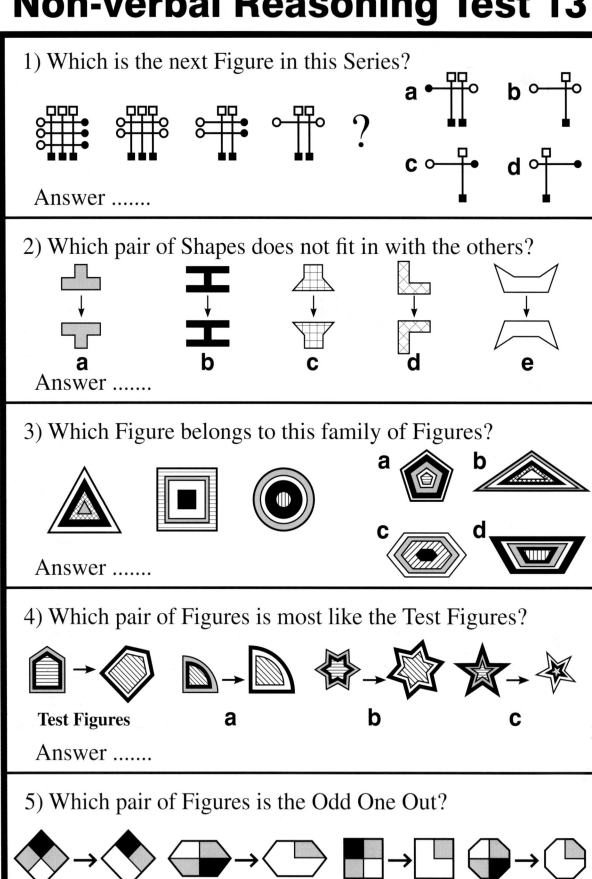

1) Which is the next Figure in this Series?

a   b   c   d

Answer ....

2) Which pair of Shapes does not fit in with the others?

a   b   c   d   e

Answer ....

3) Which Figure belongs to this family of Figures?

a   b   c   d

Answer ....

4) Which pair of Figures is most like the Test Figures?

Test Figures   a   b   c

Answer ....

5) Which pair of Figures is the Odd One Out?

a   b   c   d

Answer ....

© 2010 Stephen Curran

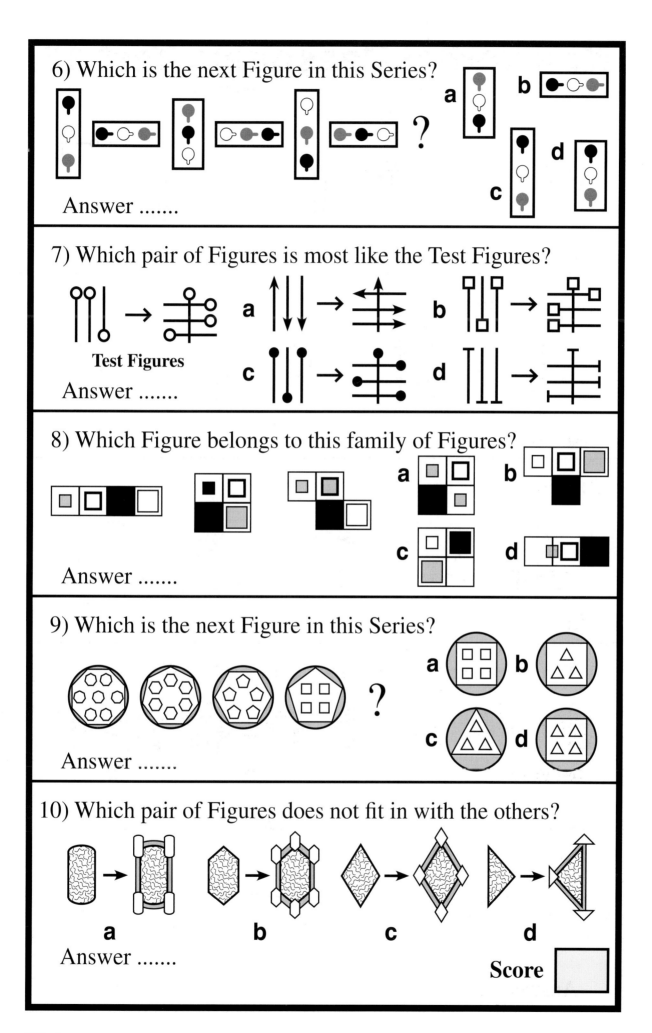

6) Which is the next Figure in this Series?

a   b   c   d

Answer ....

7) Which pair of Figures is most like the Test Figures?

Test Figures

a   b   c   d

Answer ....

8) Which Figure belongs to this family of Figures?

a   b   c   d

Answer ....

9) Which is the next Figure in this Series?

?

a   b   c   d

Answer ....

10) Which pair of Figures does not fit in with the others?

a   b   c   d

Answer ....

Score

ae © 2010 Stephen Curran

Non-verbal Reasoning Test 14

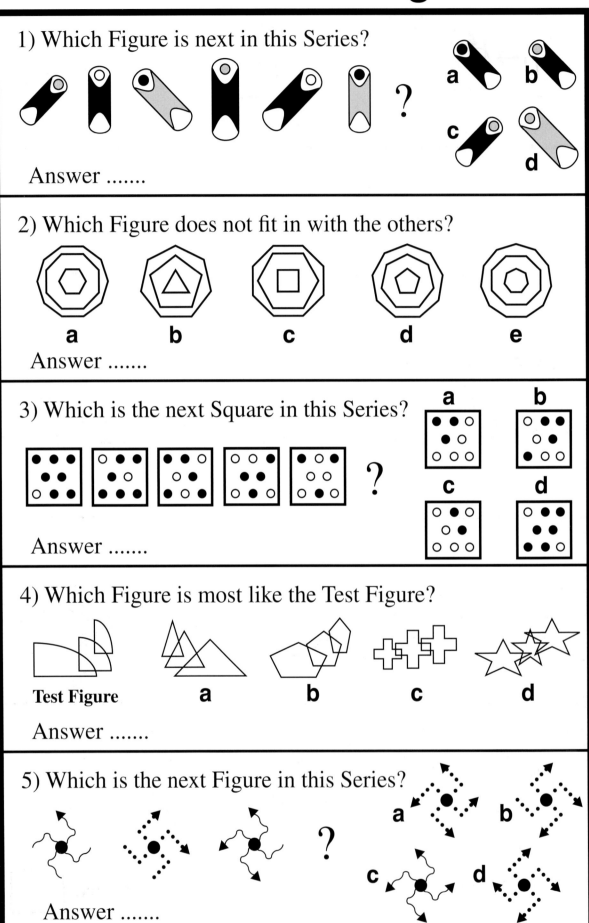

1) Which Figure is next in this Series?

a   b

c

d

Answer ....

2) Which Figure does not fit in with the others?

a   b   c   d   e

Answer ....

3) Which is the next Square in this Series?

a   b

c   d

?

Answer ....

4) Which Figure is most like the Test Figure?

Test Figure   a   b   c   d

Answer ....

5) Which is the next Figure in this Series?

?

a   b

c   d

Answer ....

© 2010 Stephen Curran

6) Which pair of Figures does not fit in with the others?

a　　　　b　　　　c　　　　d

Answer ....

7) Which pair of Figures is most like the Test Figures?

Test Figures　　　a　　　　b　　　　c

Answer ....

8) Which pair of Figures does not fit in with the others?

a　　　　b　　　　c　　　　d

Answer ....

9) Which Figure belongs to this family of Figures?

a　　　　b　　　　c

Answer ....

10) Which Figure does not fit in with the others?

a　　　　b　　　　c　　　　d　　　　e

Answer ....

Score [　　]

ae © 2010 Stephen Curran

Non-verbal Reasoning Test 15

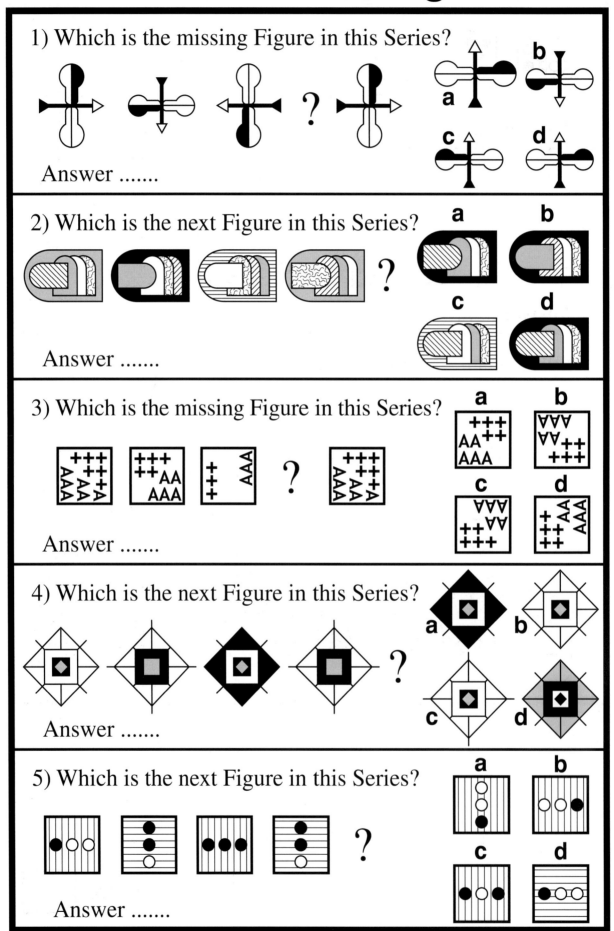

1) Which is the missing Figure in this Series?

Answer ....

2) Which is the next Figure in this Series?

Answer ....

3) Which is the missing Figure in this Series?

Answer ....

4) Which is the next Figure in this Series?

Answer ....

5) Which is the next Figure in this Series?

Answer ....

© 2010 Stephen Curran

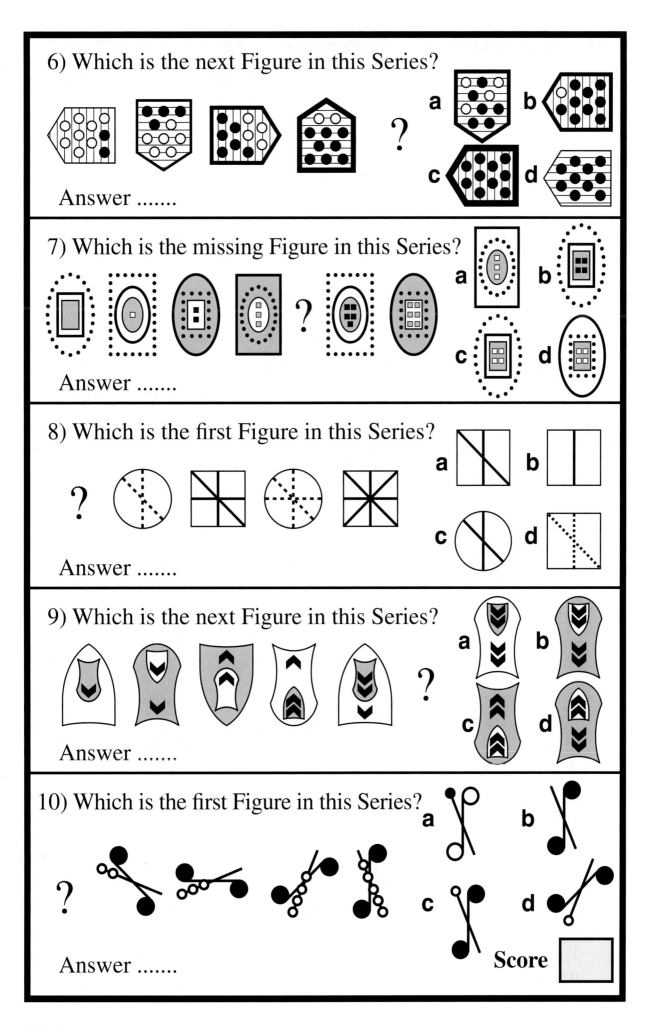

6) Which is the next Figure in this Series?

a   b

c   d

Answer ....

7) Which is the missing Figure in this Series?

a   b

c   d

Answer ....

8) Which is the first Figure in this Series?

?

a   b

c   d

Answer ....

9) Which is the next Figure in this Series?

a   b

c   d

Answer ....

10) Which is the first Figure in this Series?

a   b

?

c   d

Answer ....

Score

ae © 2010 Stephen Curran

Non-verbal Reasoning Test 16

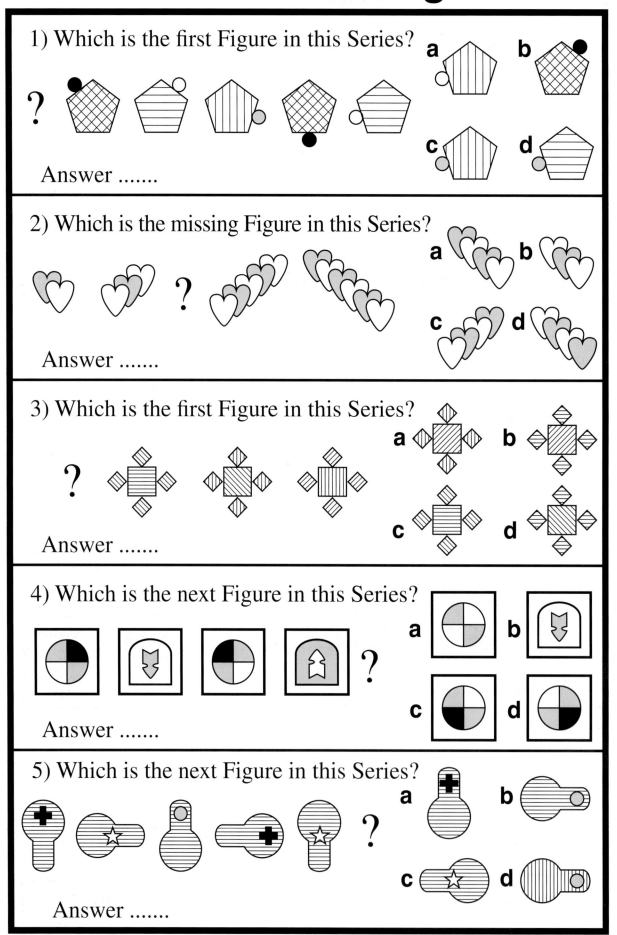

1) Which is the first Figure in this Series?

a   b   c   d

Answer ....

2) Which is the missing Figure in this Series?

a   b   c   d

Answer ....

3) Which is the first Figure in this Series?

a   b   c   d

Answer ....

4) Which is the next Figure in this Series?

a   b   c   d

Answer ....

5) Which is the next Figure in this Series?

a   b   c   d

Answer ....

© 2010 Stephen Curran

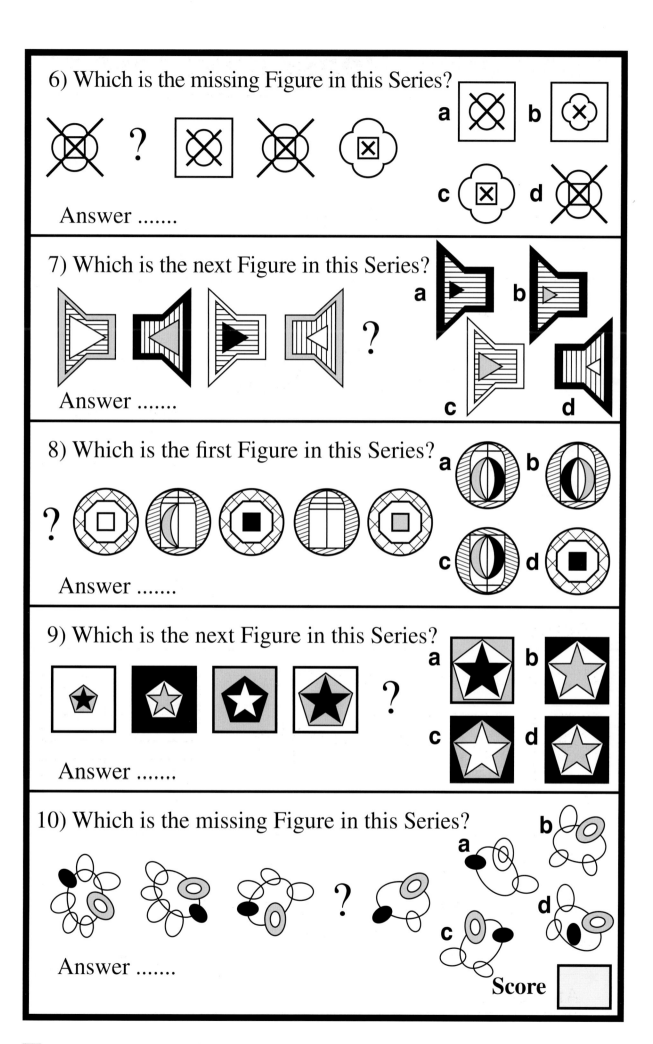

6) Which is the missing Figure in this Series?

Answer ....

7) Which is the next Figure in this Series?

Answer ....

8) Which is the first Figure in this Series?

Answer ....

9) Which is the next Figure in this Series?

Answer ....

10) Which is the missing Figure in this Series?

Answer ....

Score

© 2010 Stephen Curran

Non-verbal Reasoning Test 17
Odd One Out

In each of the rows below there are five Figures. Find one Figure in each row that is **most unlike** the other four.

Example

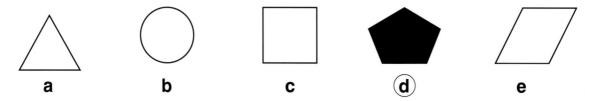

Now do the questions below. Circle the correct answer.

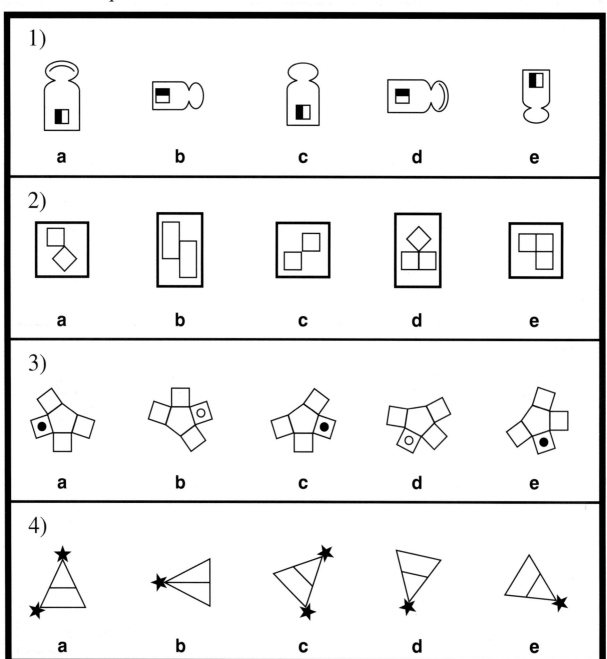

© 2010 Stephen Curran

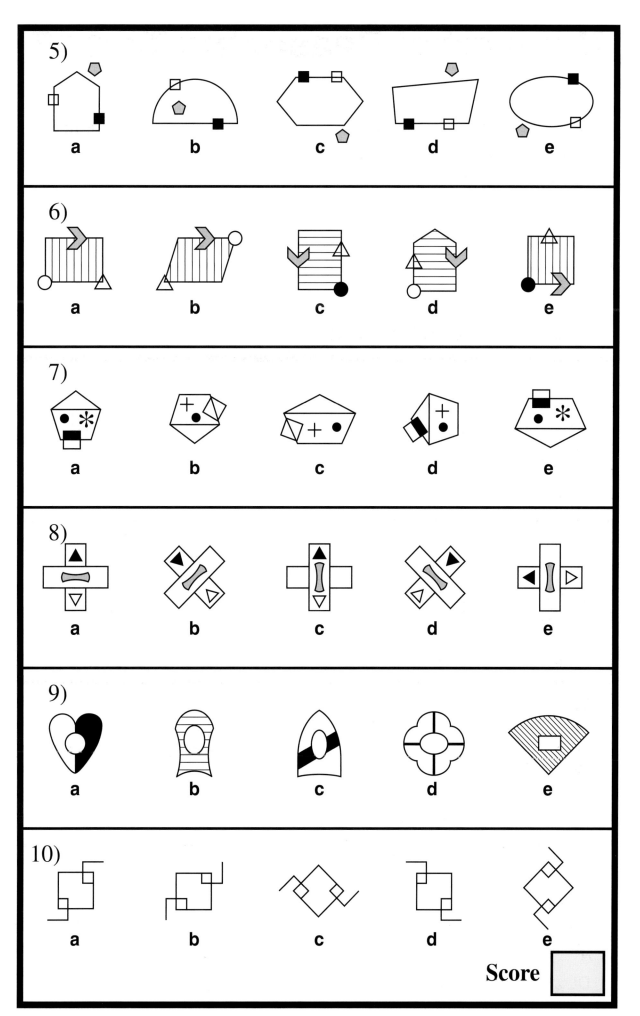

© 2010 Stephen Curran

Non-verbal Reasoning Test 18
Codes

The following Shapes correspond to the codes below them. You must decide how the code letters go with the Shapes and then find the correct code for the Test Shape.

Example

TEST SHAPE

				BR	AS	AT	BS	AR
AR	BS	BT		(a)	b	c	d	e

The **first letter** stands for the type of Fill: **A** - White Fill; **B** - Shaded Fill.

The **second letter** stands for each Shape: **R** -Triangle; **S** - Arrow; **T** - Circle.

The answer is **BR**: **B** for Shaded Fill; **R** for Triangle.

Now do the questions below. Circle the correct answer.

1)

TEST SHAPE

	KC	LA	JD
	a	b	c
	JC	MB	
	d	e	

JA	KB	LC	MA	KD

2)

TEST SHAPE

	YR	WT	XT
	a	b	c
	YS	XR	
	d	e	

XS	YT	WR	XQ	WS

3)

TEST SHAPE

	GY	FY	EY
	a	b	c
	EX	FZ	
	d	e	

GZ	EY	FX	HY	GW

4)

TEST SHAPE

	BN	CK	DN
	a	b	c
	AL	CL	
	d	e	

DL	BM	CN	BK	AM

© 2010 Stephen Curran

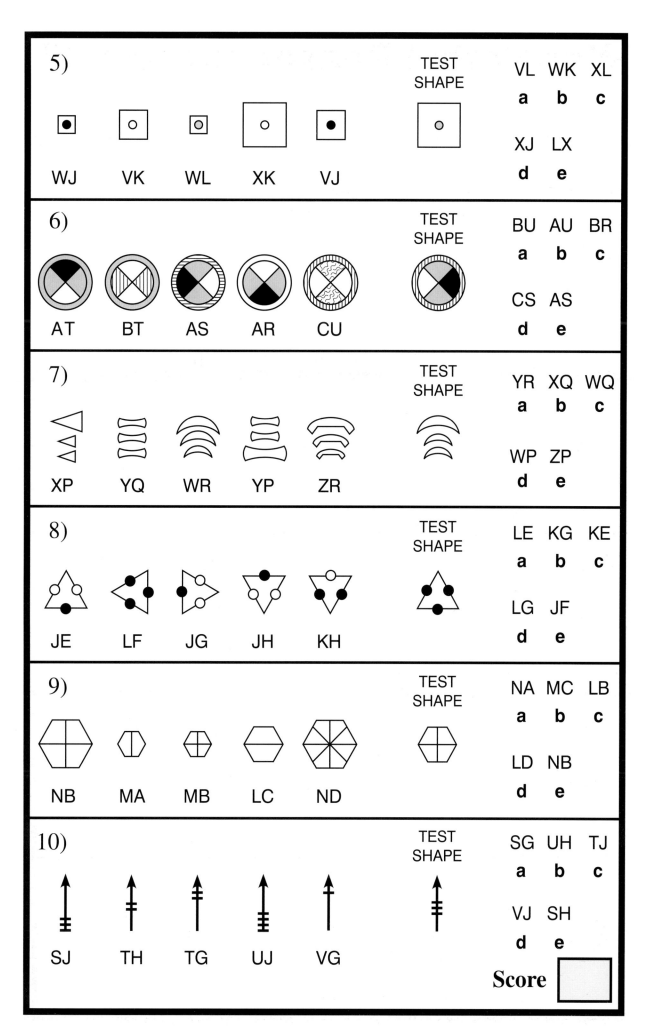

5) | TEST SHAPE | VL **a** | WK **b** | XL **c** |
| XJ **d** | LX **e** |

WJ | VK | WL | XK | VJ

6) | TEST SHAPE | BU **a** | AU **b** | BR **c** |
| CS **d** | AS **e** |

AT | BT | AS | AR | CU

7) | TEST SHAPE | YR **a** | XQ **b** | WQ **c** |
| WP **d** | ZP **e** |

XP | YQ | WR | YP | ZR

8) | TEST SHAPE | LE **a** | KG **b** | KE **c** |
| LG **d** | JF **e** |

JE | LF | JG | JH | KH

9) | TEST SHAPE | NA **a** | MC **b** | LB **c** |
| LD **d** | NB **e** |

NB | MA | MB | LC | ND

10) | TEST SHAPE | SG **a** | UH **b** | TJ **c** |
| VJ **d** | SH **e** |

SJ | TH | TG | UJ | VG

Score

ae © 2010 Stephen Curran

Non-verbal Reasoning Test 19
Analogies

On the left of each row are two Shapes with an arrow between them. Decide how the second Shape is related to the first. After these there is a third Shape, then an arrow and then five more Shapes. Decide which of the five Shapes goes with the **third** Shape to **make a pair** like the two Shapes on the left.

Example

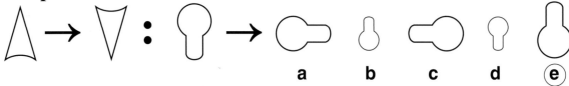

Now do the questions below. Circle the correct answer.

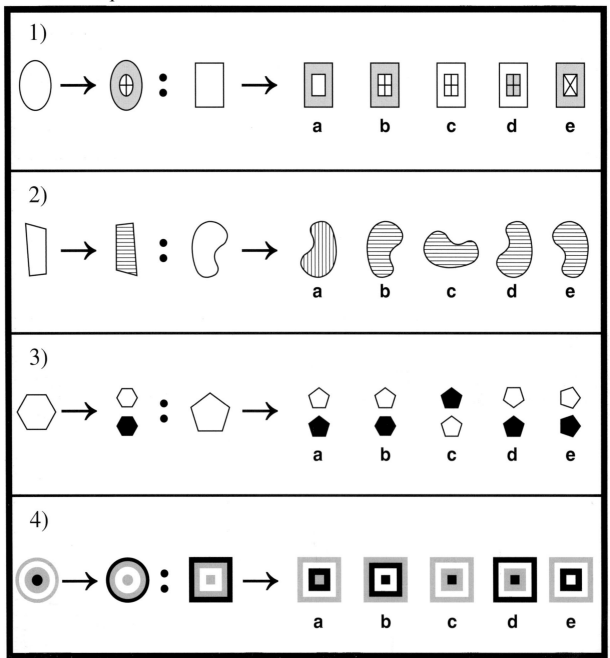

© 2010 Stephen Curran

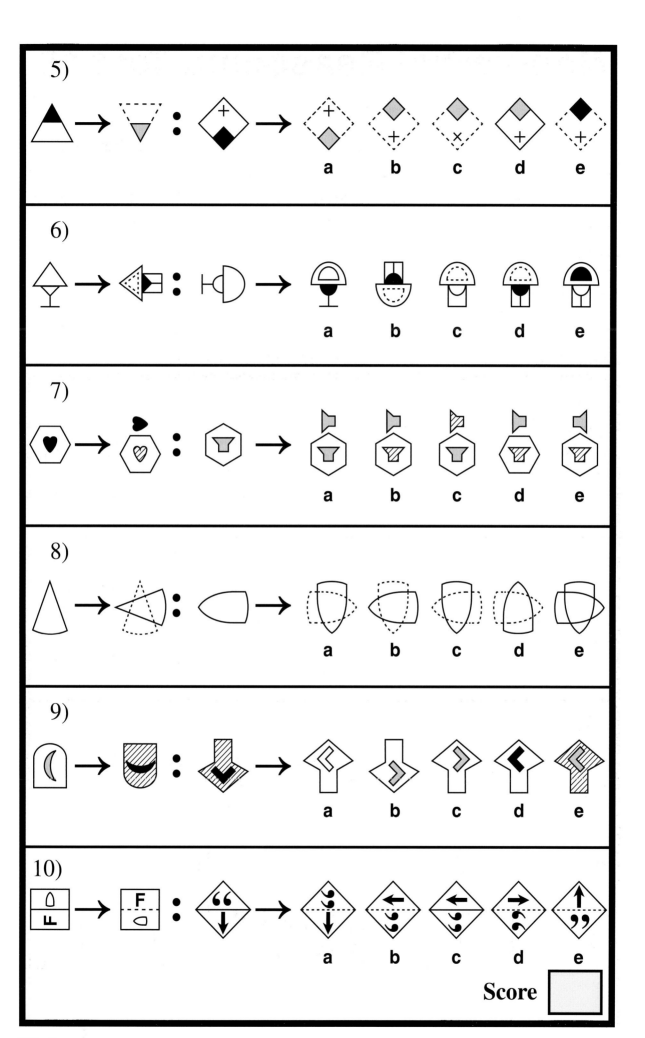

© 2010 Stephen Curran

Non-verbal Reasoning Test 20
Similarities

On the left of each of the rows below there are two Figures that are alike. On the right there are five more Figures. Find which one of these five is **most like** the two Figures on the left.

Example

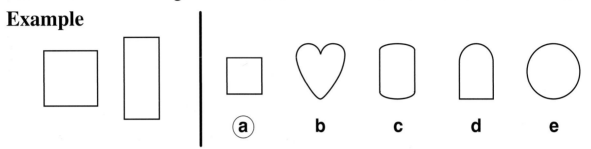

Now do the questions below. Circle the correct answer.

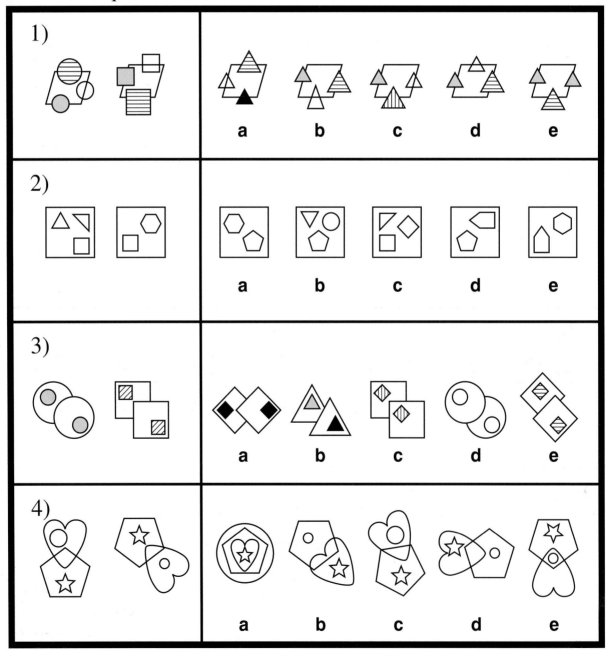

© 2010 Stephen Curran

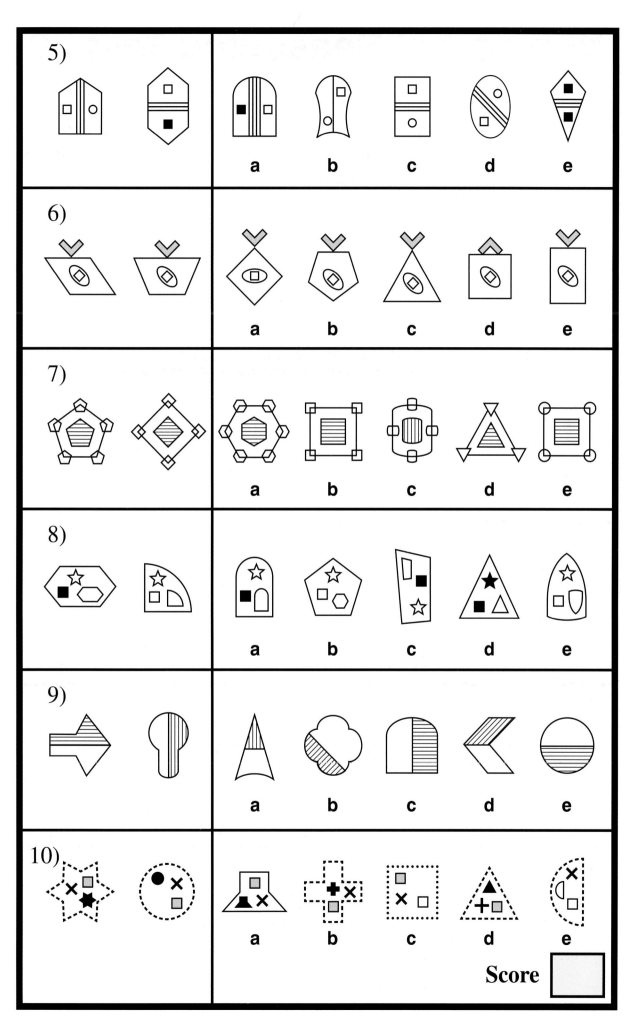

Non-verbal Reasoning Test 21
Series

To the left of each of the lines below there are five squares arranged in order. One of these squares has been left empty. Find which one of the five squares on the right should take the place of the empty square.

Example

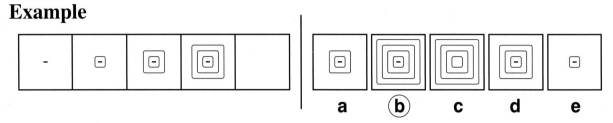

Now do the questions below. Circle the correct answer.

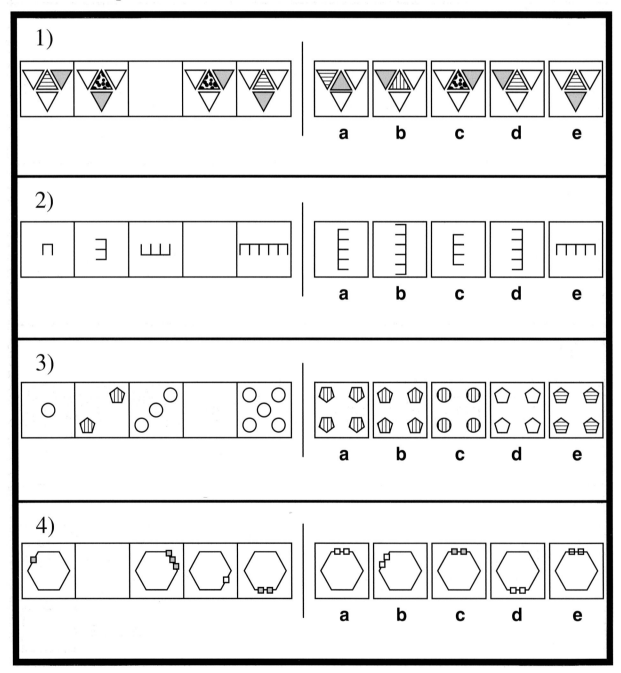

© 2010 Stephen Curran

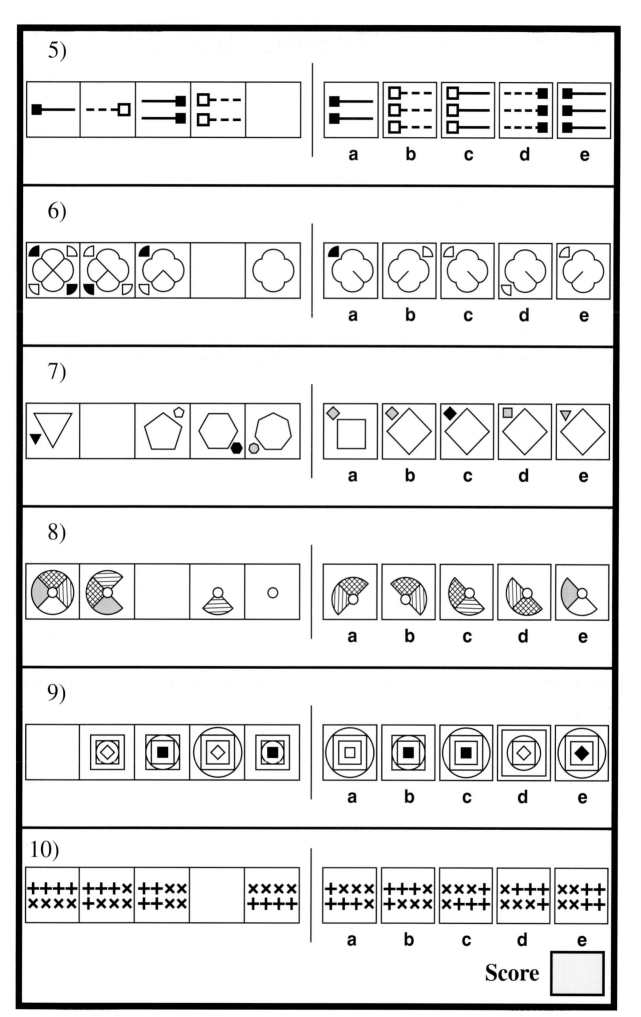

© 2010 Stephen Curran

Non-verbal Reasoning Test 22
Matrices

In the big square on the left of each line below, one of the small squares has been left empty. One of the five Figures on the right should fill the empty square. Find this Figure.

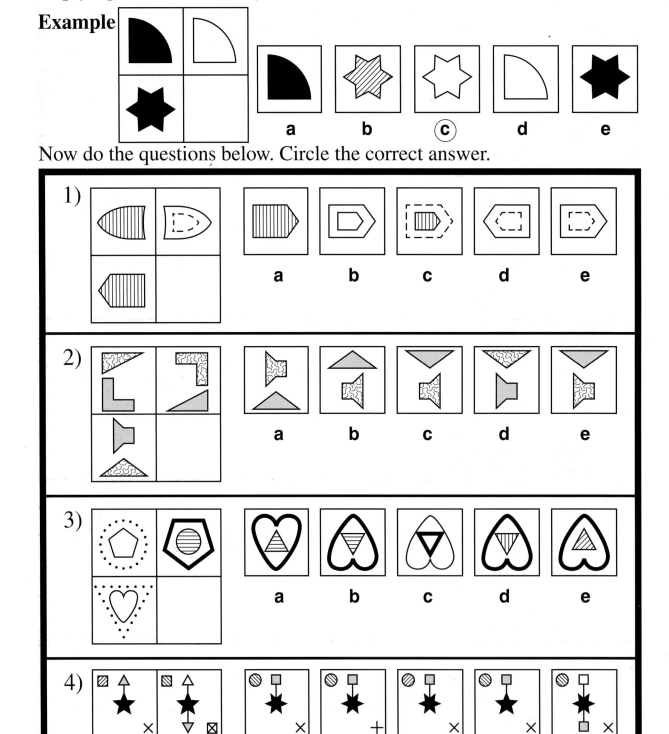

Now do the questions below. Circle the correct answer.

 © 2010 Stephen Curran

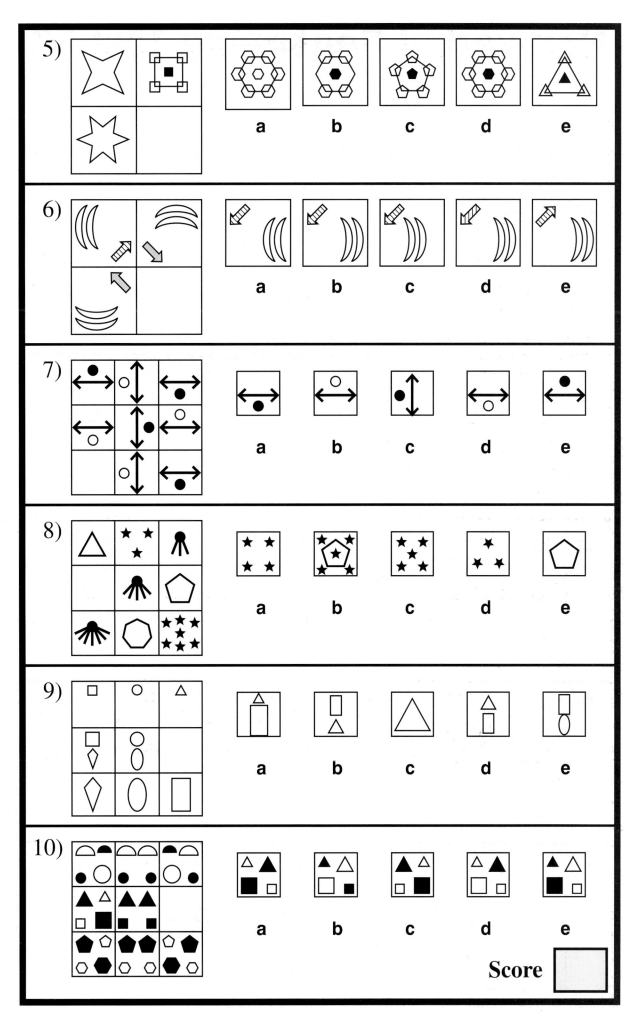

Non-verbal Reasoning Test 23
Odd One Out

In each of the rows below there are five Figures. Find one Figure in each row that is **most unlike** the other four.

Example

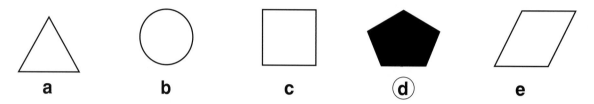

Now do the questions below. Circle the correct answer.

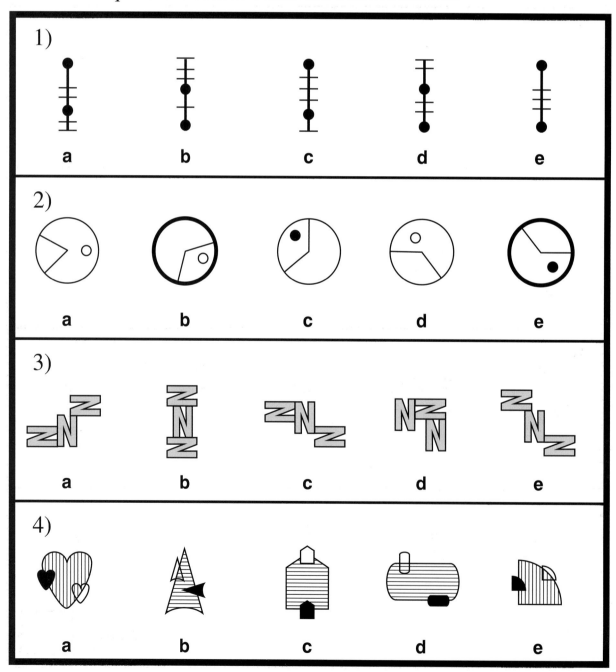

© 2010 Stephen Curran

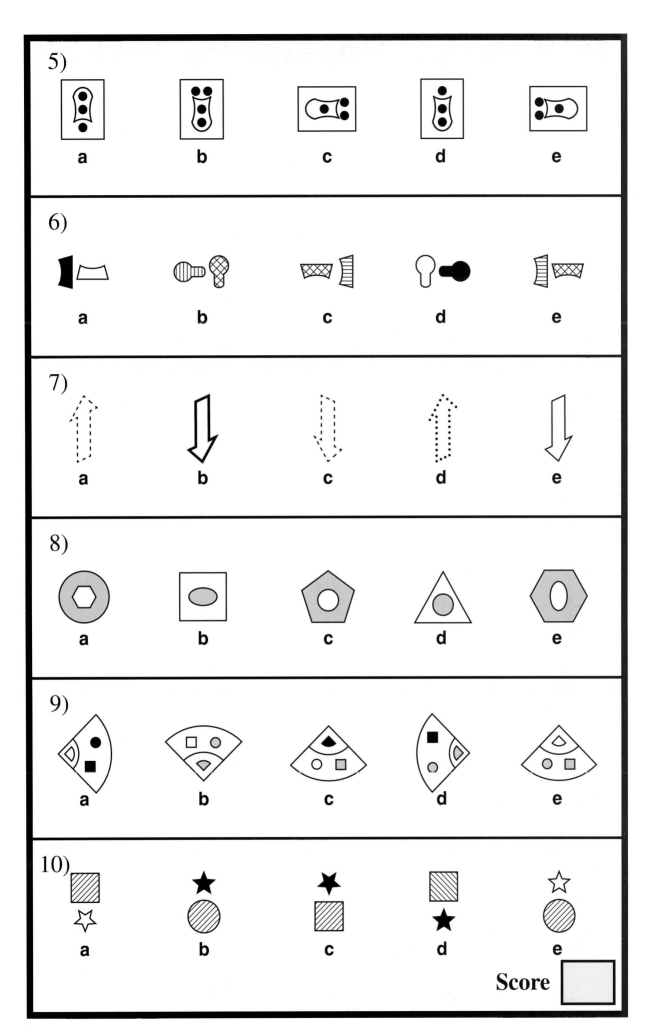

ae © 2010 Stephen Curran

Non-verbal Reasoning Test 24
Codes

The following Shapes correspond to the codes next to them. You must decide how the code letters go with the Shapes and then find the correct code for the Test Shape.

Example

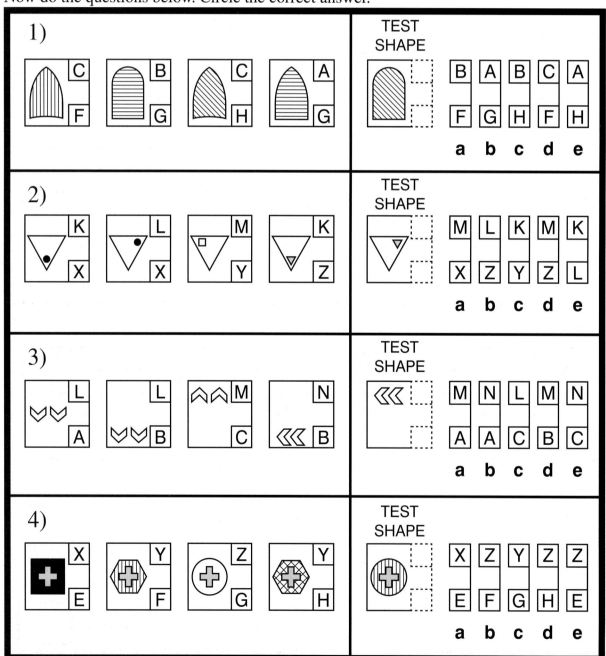

The **top letter** stands for each Shape: **Q** - Isosceles Trapezium Shape; **R** - Ordinary Trapezium Shape. The **bottom letter** stands for the type of Fill: **H** - White Fill; **I** - Grey Fill; **J** - Black Fill. The answer is **RI**.

Now do the questions below. Circle the correct answer.

© 2010 Stephen Curran

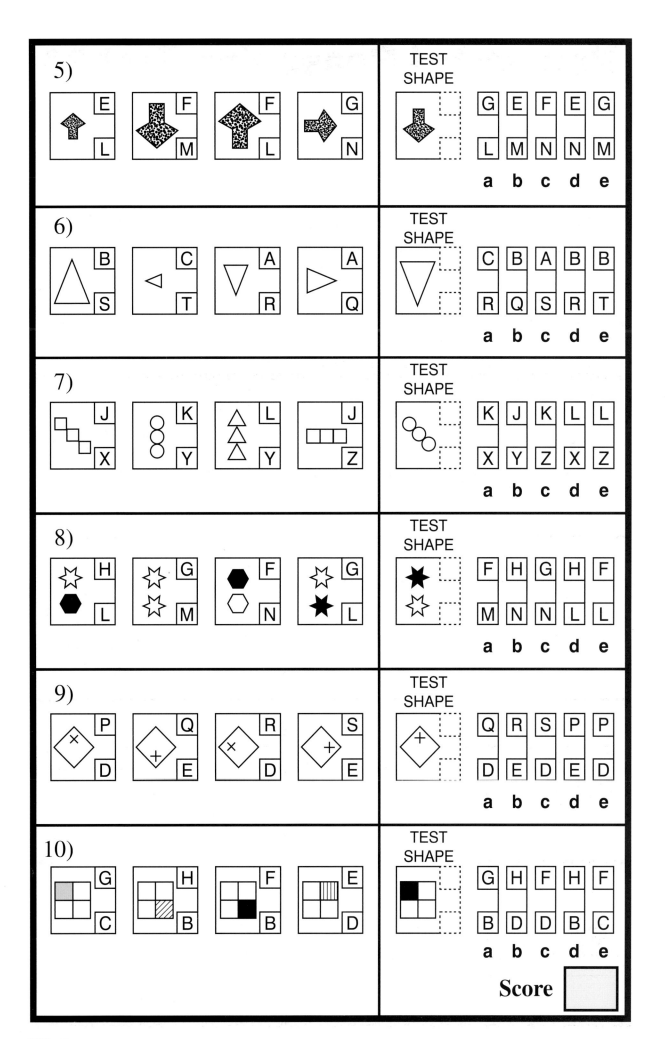

5)

TEST SHAPE					
	G	E	F	E	G
	L	M	N	N	M
	a	b	c	d	e

6)

TEST SHAPE					
	C	B	A	B	B
	R	Q	S	R	T
	a	b	c	d	e

7)

TEST SHAPE					
	K	J	K	L	L
	X	Y	Z	X	Z
	a	b	c	d	e

8)

TEST SHAPE					
	F	H	G	H	F
	M	N	N	L	L
	a	b	c	d	e

9)

TEST SHAPE					
	Q	R	S	P	P
	D	E	D	E	D
	a	b	c	d	e

10)

TEST SHAPE					
	G	H	F	H	F
	B	D	D	B	C
	a	b	c	d	e

Score

© 2010 Stephen Curran

Non-verbal Reasoning Test 25
Analogies

On the left of each row are two Shapes with an arrow between them. Decide how the second Shape is related to the first. After these there is a third Shape, then an arrow and then five more Shapes. Decide which of the five Shapes goes with the **third** Shape to **make a pair** like the two Shapes on the left.

Example

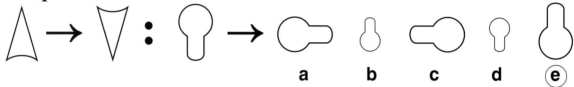

Now do the questions below. Circle the correct answer.

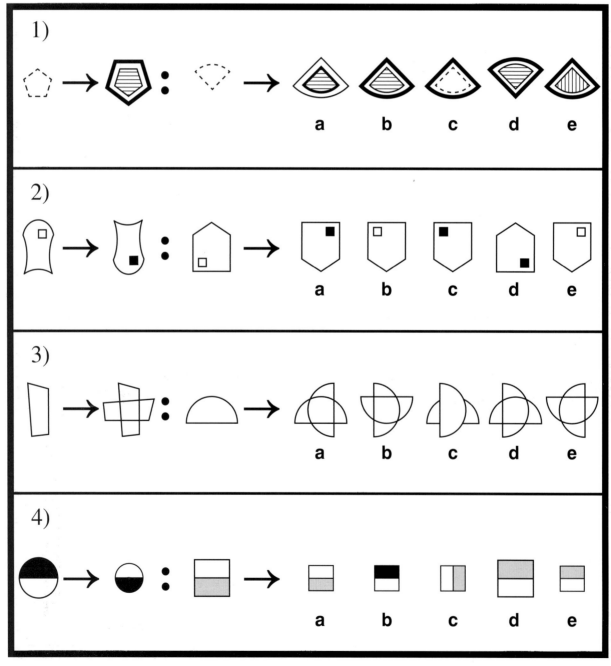

© 2010 Stephen Curran

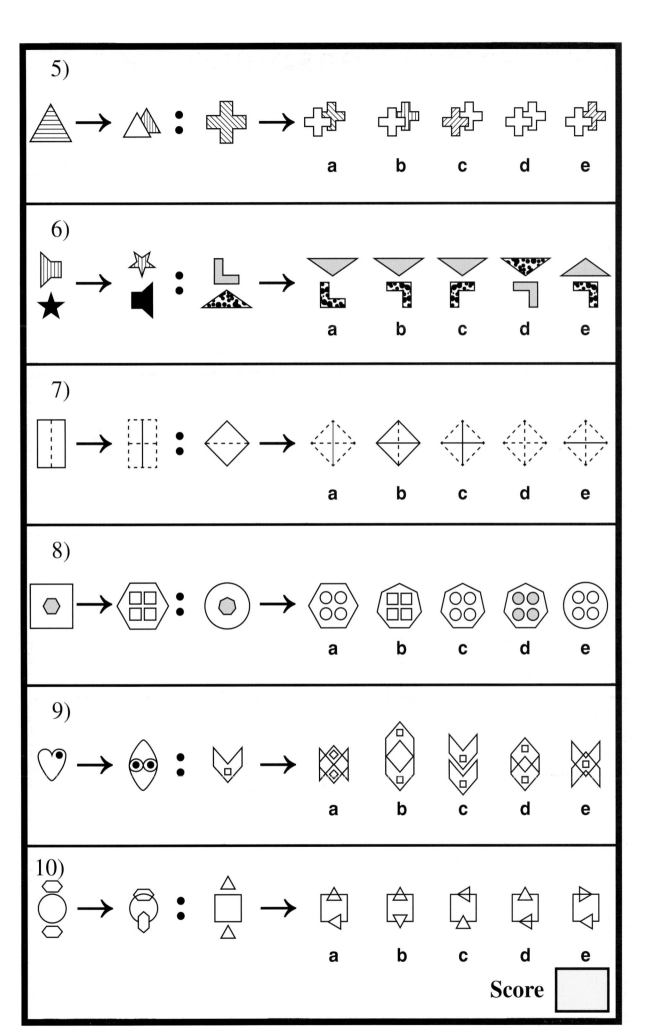

5)

a   b   c   d   e

6)

a   b   c   d   e

7)

a   b   c   d   e

8)

a   b   c   d   e

9)

a   b   c   d   e

10)

a   b   c   d   e

Score

ae © 2010 Stephen Curran

Non-verbal Reasoning Test 26
Similarities

On the left of each of the rows below there are two Figures that are alike. On the right there are five more Figures. Find which one of these five is **most like** the two Figures on the left.

Example

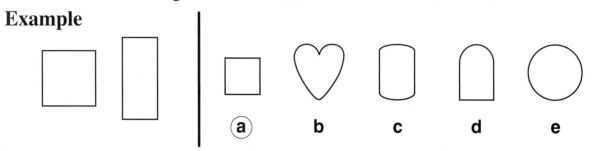

Now do the questions below. Circle the correct answer.

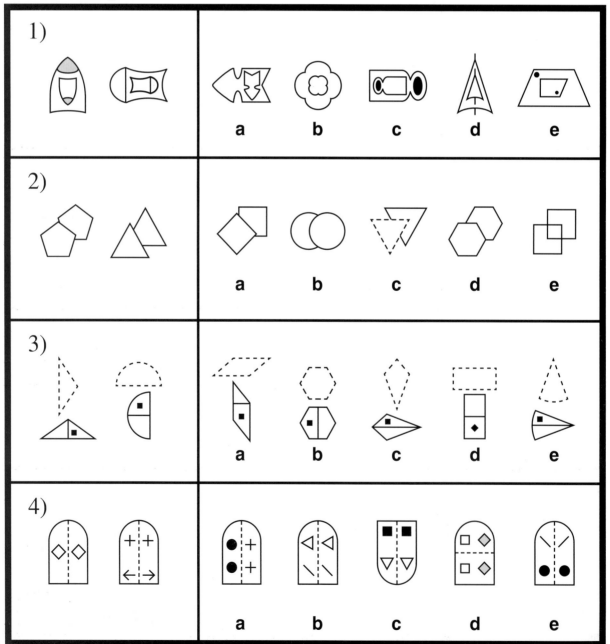

© 2010 Stephen Curran

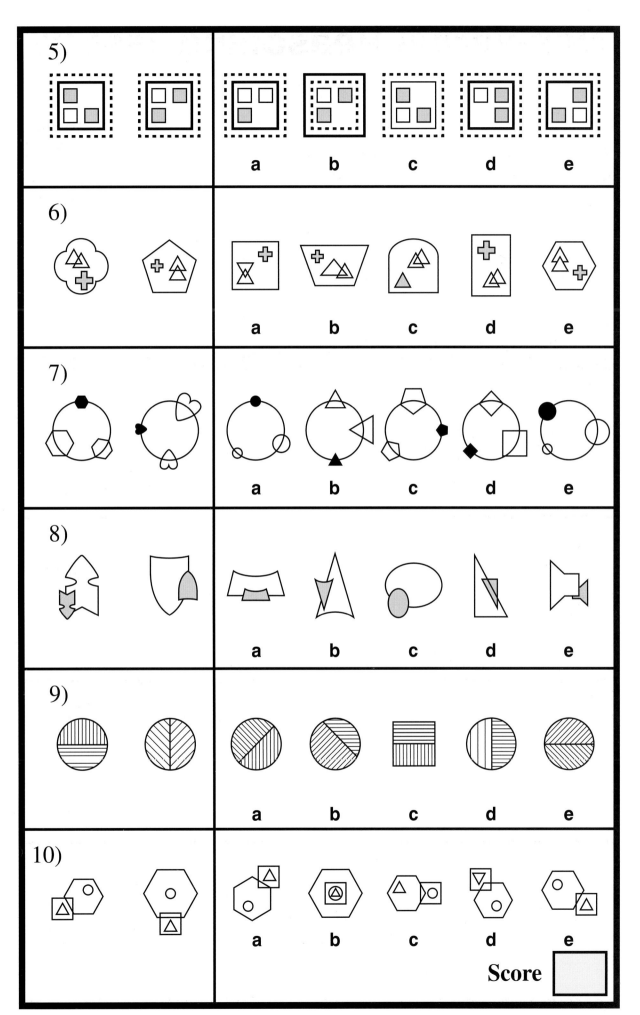

5)

             a   b   c   d   e

6)

             a   b   c   d   e

7)

             a   b   c   d   e

8)

             a   b   c   d   e

9)

             a   b   c   d   e

10)

             a   b   c   d   e

Score

ae © 2010 Stephen Curran

Non-verbal Reasoning Test 27
Series

To the left of each of the lines below there are five squares arranged in order. One of these squares has been left empty. Find which one of the five squares on the right should take the place of the empty square.

Example

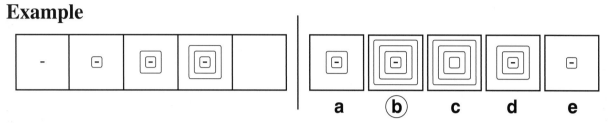

Now do the questions below. Circle the correct answer.

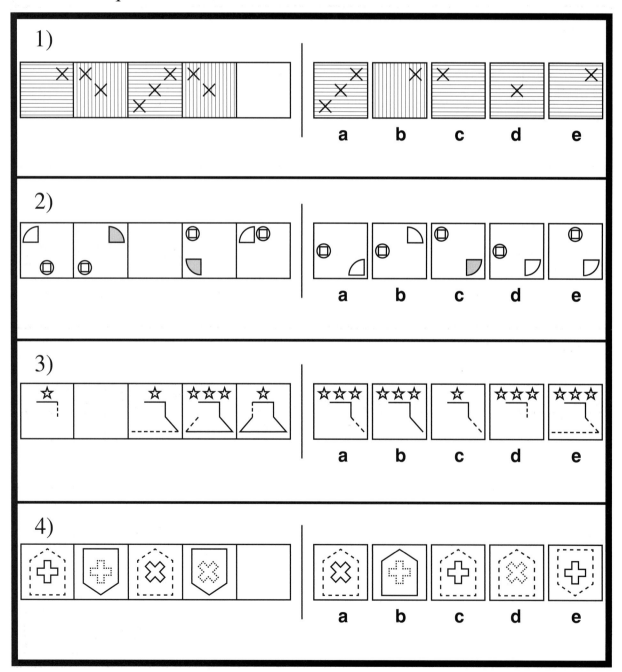

© 2010 Stephen Curran

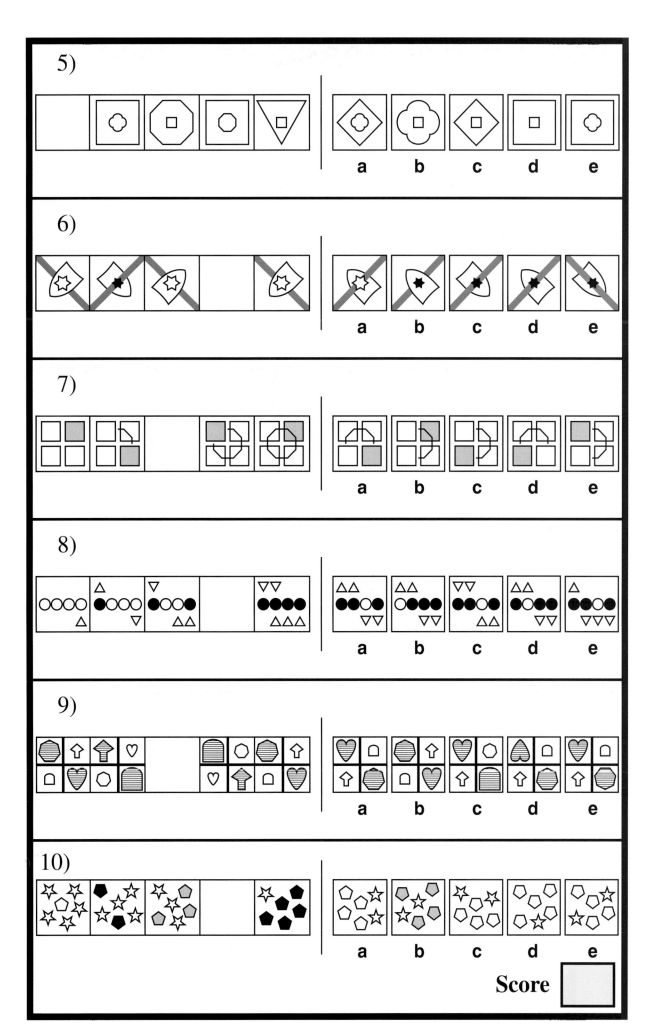

5)

6)

7)

8)

9)

10)

Score

Non-verbal Reasoning Test 28
Matrices

In the big square on the left of each line below, one of the small squares has been left empty. One of the five Figures on the right should fill the empty square. Find this Figure.

Example

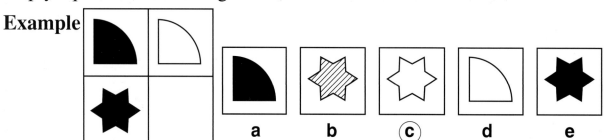

a   b   ⓒ   d   e

Now do the questions below. Circle the correct answer.

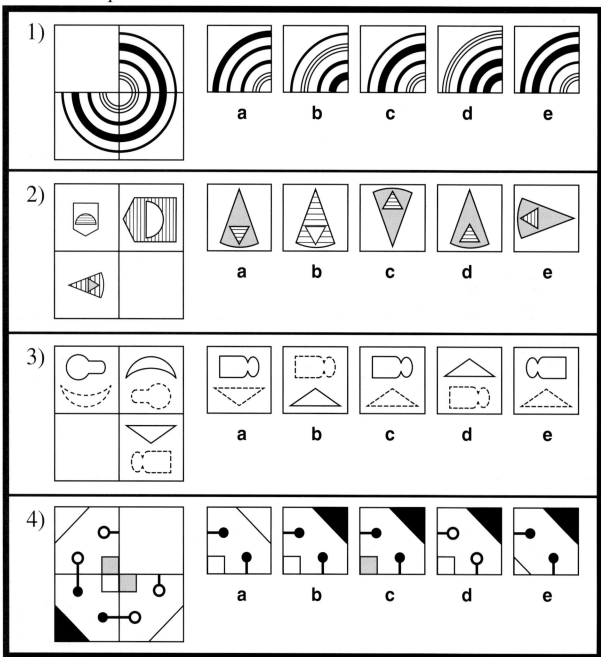

© 2010 Stephen Curran

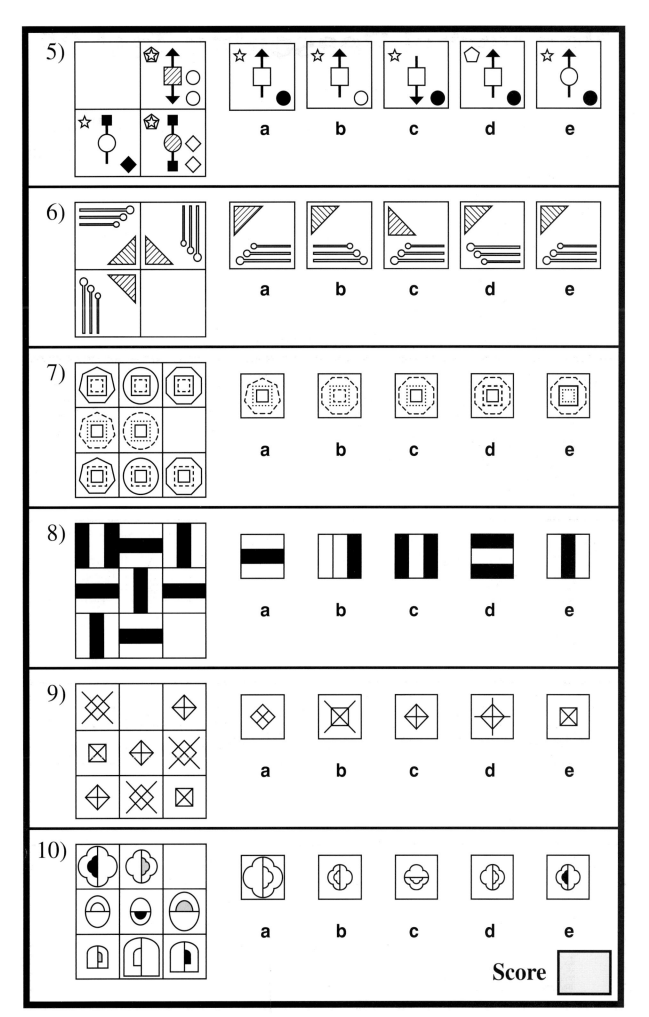

ae © 2010 Stephen Curran

Non-verbal Reasoning Test 29
Odd One Out

In each of the rows below there are five Figures. Find one Figure in each row that is **most unlike** the other four.

Example

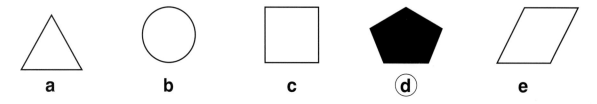

Now do the questions below. Circle the correct answer.

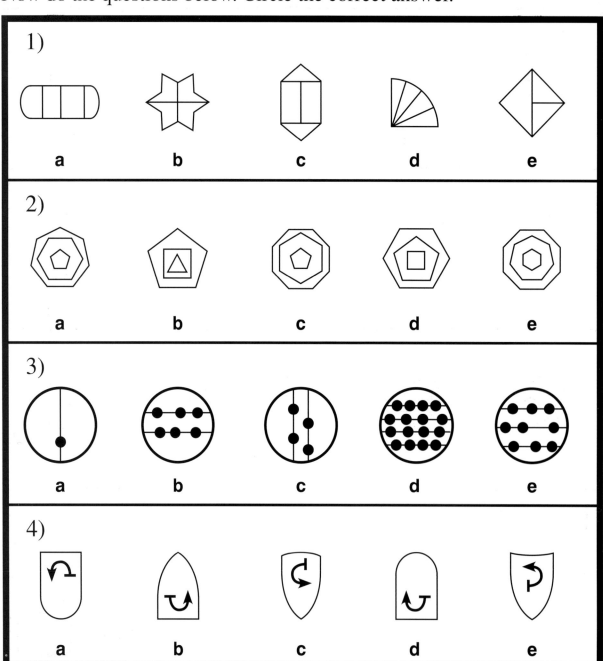

© 2010 Stephen Curran

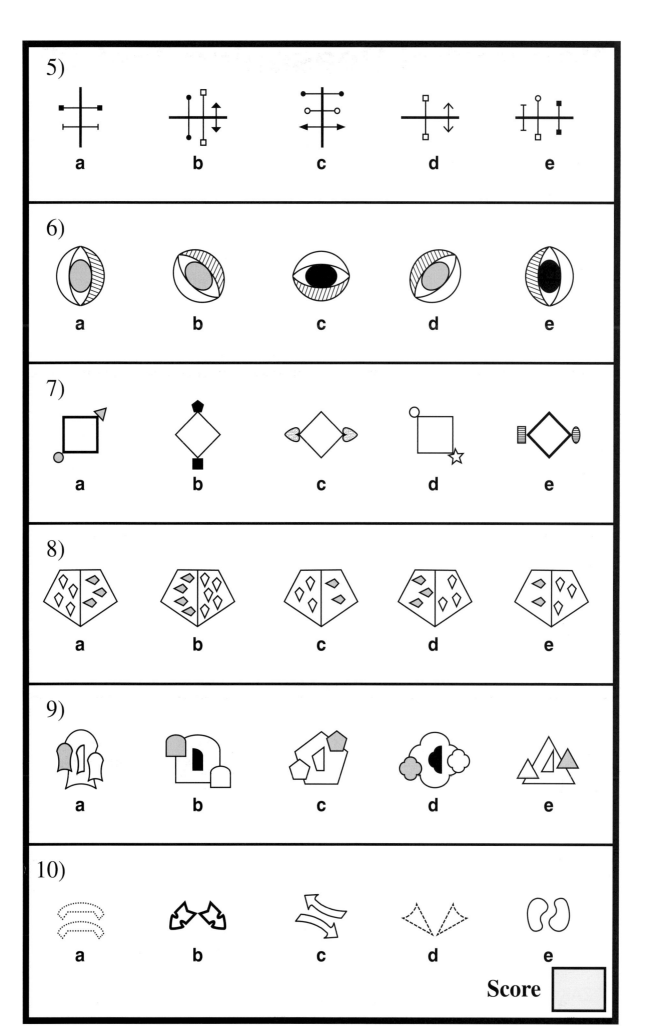

5)   a   b   c   d   e

6)   a   b   c   d   e

7)   a   b   c   d   e

8)   a   b   c   d   e

9)   a   b   c   d   e

10)   a   b   c   d   e

Score

© 2010 Stephen Curran

Non-verbal Reasoning Test 30
Codes

The following Shapes correspond to the codes below them. You must decide how the code letters go with the Shapes and then find the correct code for the Test Shape.

Example

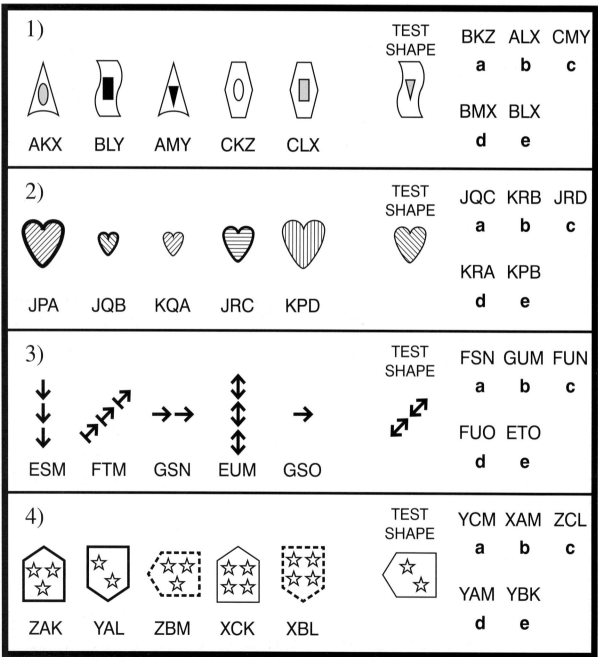

The **first letter** stands for the type of Fill: **A** - White Fill; **B** - Shaded Fill.
The **second letter** stands for each Shape: **R** -Triangle; **S** - Arrow; **T** - Circle.
The answer is **BR**: **B** for Shaded Fill; **R** for Triangle.

Now do the questions below. Circle the correct answer.

© 2010 Stephen Curran **ae**

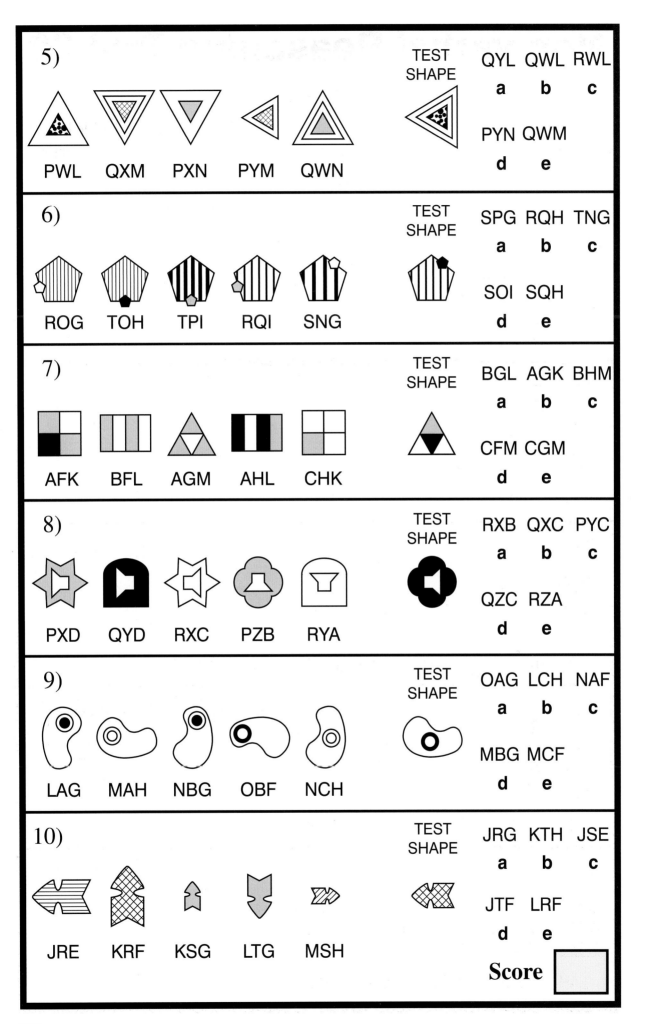

5)

TEST SHAPE

QYL	QWL	RWL
a	b	c

PYN	QWM	
d	e	

PWL   QXM   PXN   PYM   QWN

6)

TEST SHAPE

SPG	RQH	TNG
a	b	c

SOI	SQH	
d	e	

ROG   TOH   TPI   RQI   SNG

7)

TEST SHAPE

BGL	AGK	BHM
a	b	c

CFM	CGM	
d	e	

AFK   BFL   AGM   AHL   CHK

8)

TEST SHAPE

RXB	QXC	PYC
a	b	c

QZC	RZA	
d	e	

PXD   QYD   RXC   PZB   RYA

9)

TEST SHAPE

OAG	LCH	NAF
a	b	c

MBG	MCF	
d	e	

LAG   MAH   NBG   OBF   NCH

10)

TEST SHAPE

JRG	KTH	JSE
a	b	c

JTF	LRF	
d	e	

JRE   KRF   KSG   LTG   MSH

Score

ae © 2010 Stephen Curran

Non-verbal Reasoning Test 31
Analogies

On the left of each row are two Shapes with an arrow between them. Decide how the second Shape is related to the first. After these there is a third Shape, then an arrow and then five more Shapes. Decide which of the five Shapes goes with the **third** Shape to **make a pair** like the two Shapes on the left.

Example

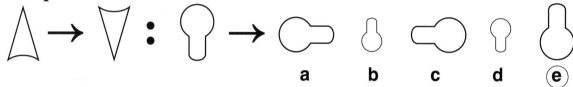

Now do the questions below. Circle the correct answer.

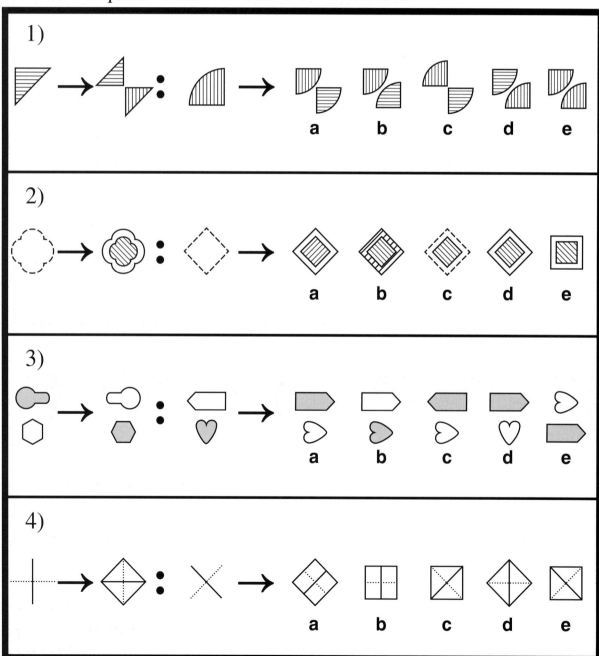

© 2010 Stephen Curran

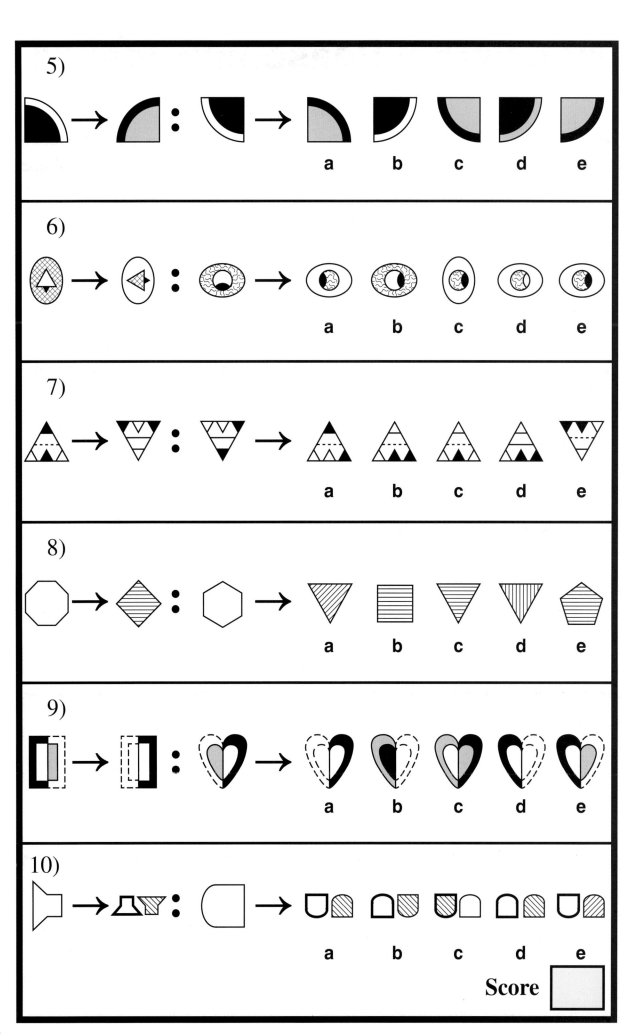

ae © 2010 Stephen Curran

Non-verbal Reasoning Test 32
Similarities

On the left of each of the rows below there are two Figures that are alike. On the right there are five more Figures. Find which one of these five is **most like** the two Figures on the left.

Example

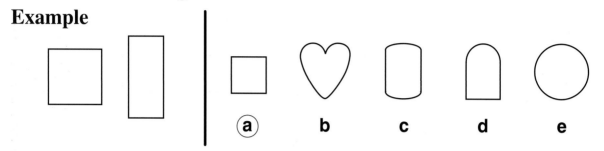

Now do the questions below. Circle the correct answer.

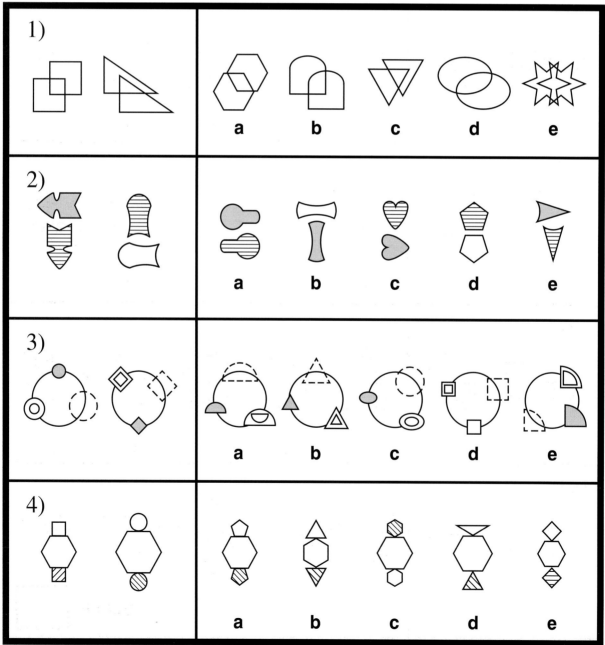

© 2010 Stephen Curran

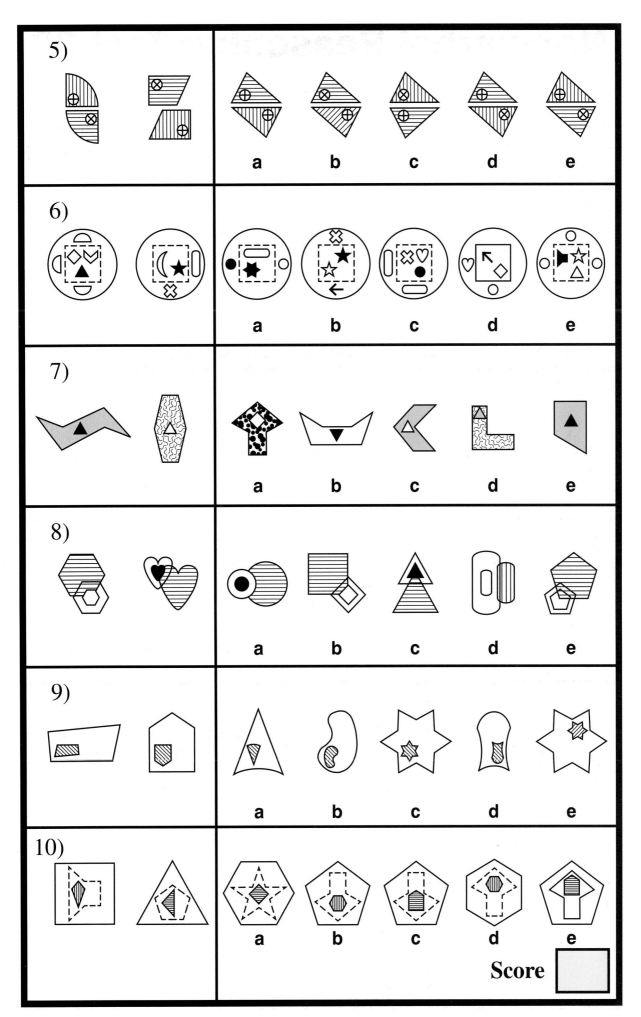

5)

    a   b   c   d   e

6)

    a   b   c   d   e

7)

    a   b   c   d   e

8)

    a   b   c   d   e

9)

    a   b   c   d   e

10)

    a   b   c   d   e

Score

Non-verbal Reasoning Test 33
Series

To the left of each of the lines below there are five squares arranged in order. One of these squares has been left empty. Find which one of the five squares on the right should take the place of the empty square.

Example

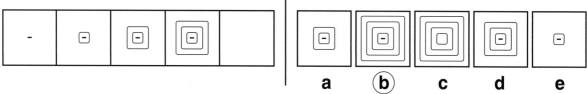

a   (b)   c   d   e

Now do the questions below. Circle the correct answer.

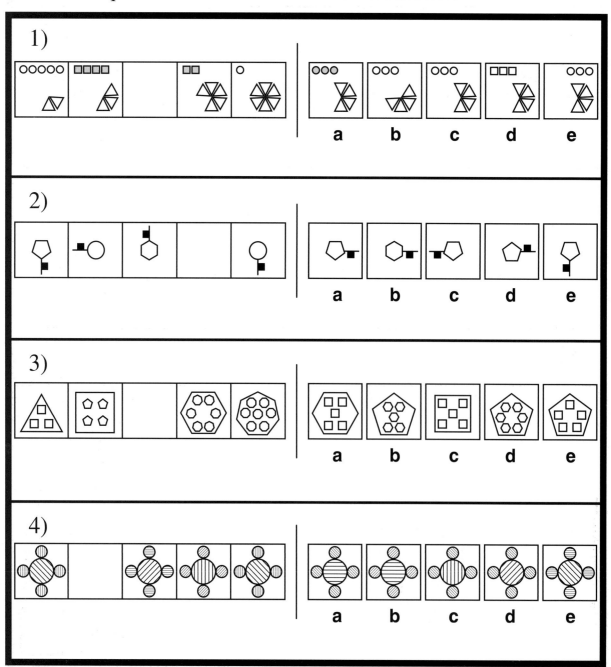

     © 2010 Stephen Curran

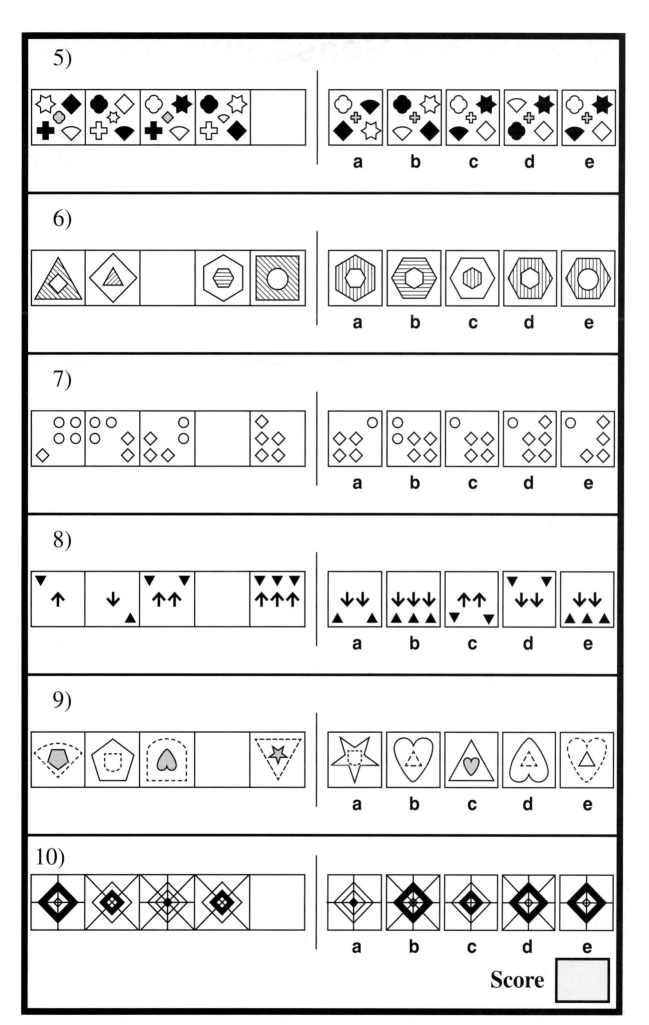

© 2010 Stephen Curran

Non-verbal Reasoning Test 34
Matrices

In the big square on the left of each line below, one of the small squares has been left empty. One of the five Figures on the right should fill the empty square. Find this Figure.

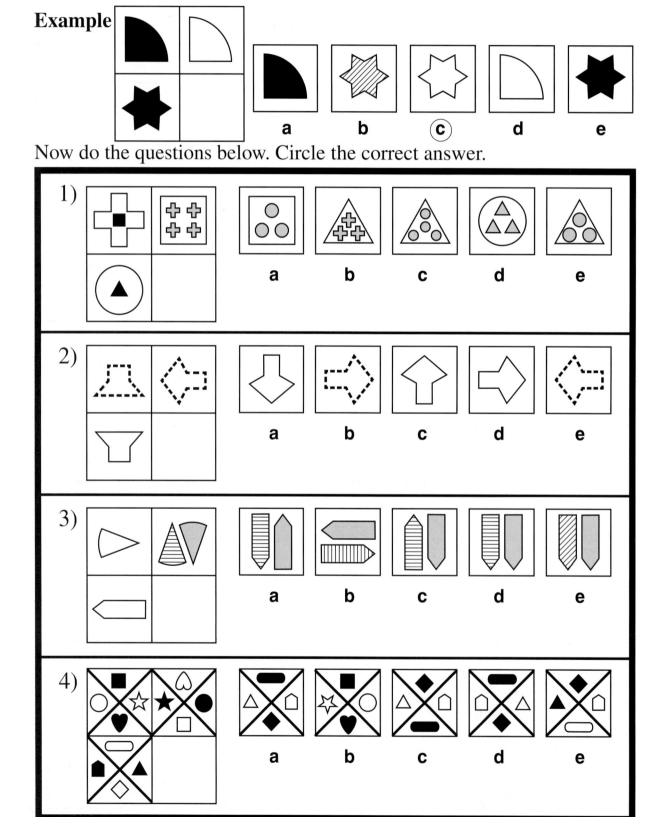

Now do the questions below. Circle the correct answer.

© 2010 Stephen Curran

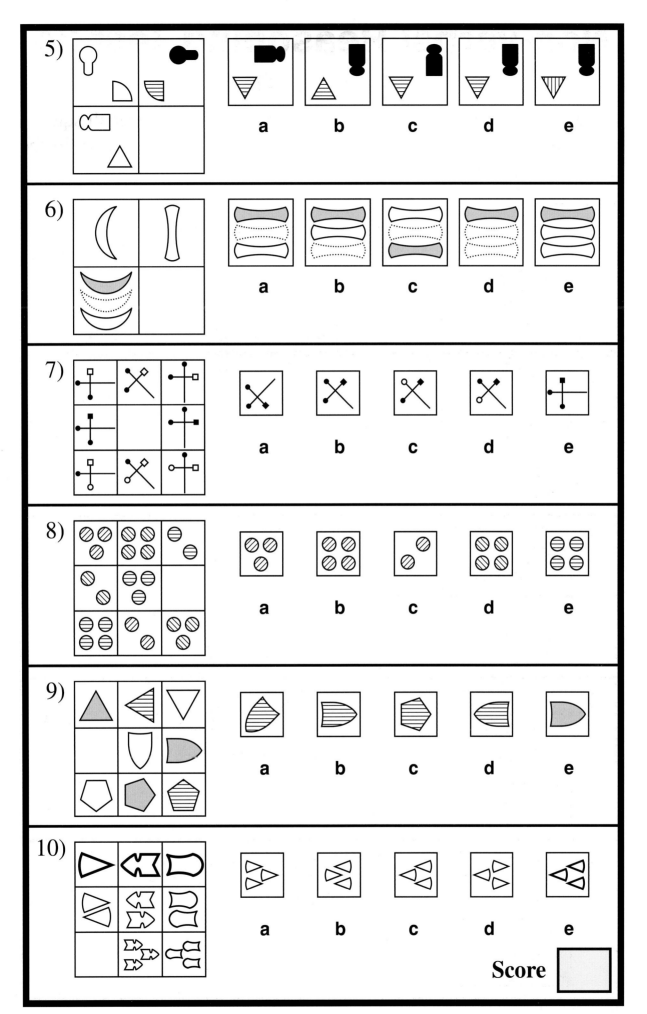

Non-verbal Reasoning Test 35
Odd One Out

In each of the rows below there are five Figures. Find one Figure in each row that is **most unlike** the other four.

Example

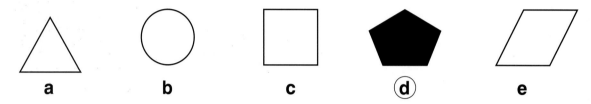

Now do the questions below. Circle the correct answer.

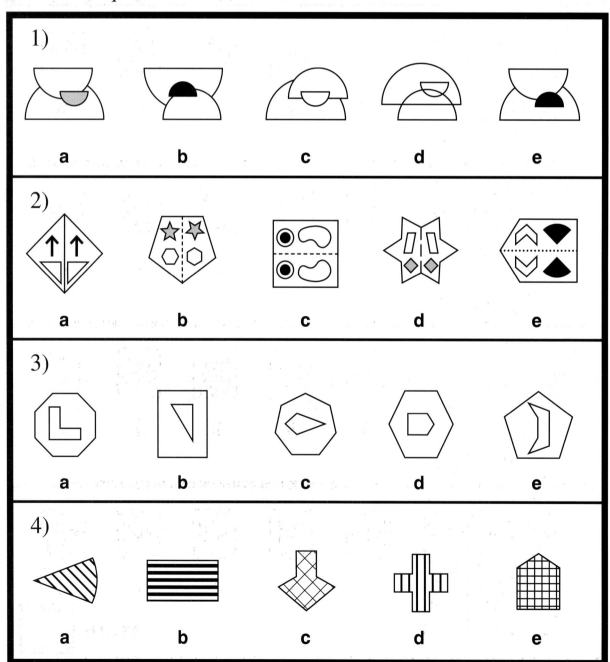

   © 2010 Stephen Curran

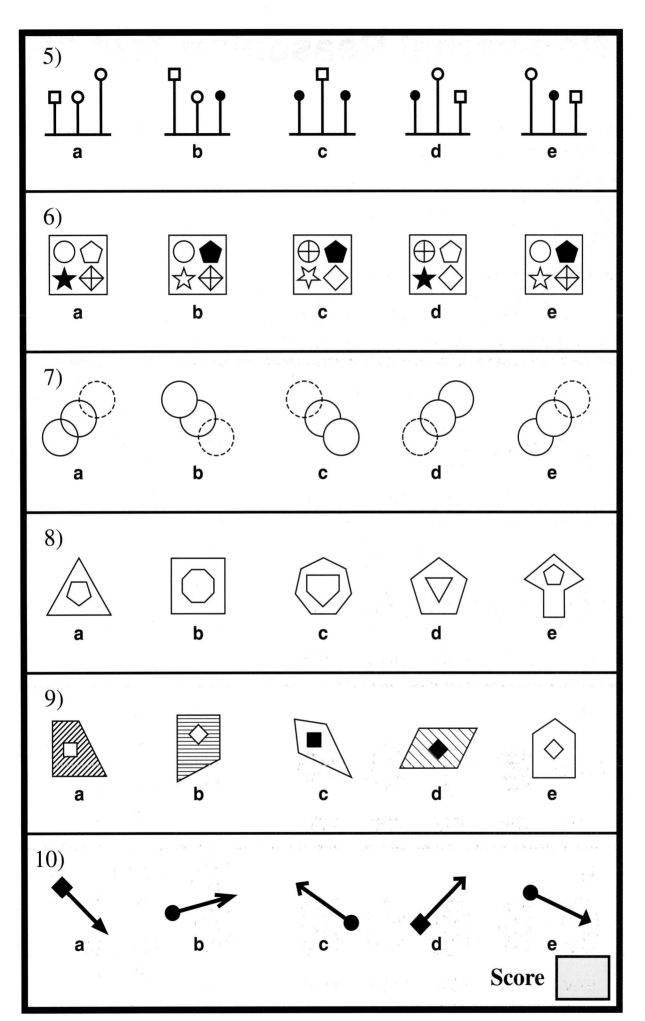

Non-verbal Reasoning Test 36
Codes

The following Shapes correspond to the codes below them. You must decide how the code letters go with the Shapes and then find the correct code for the Test Shape.

Example

TEST SHAPE

△ AR   ⬆ BS   ⊘ BT   △ (test)

BR   AS   AT   BS   AR
(a)   b   c   d   e

The **first letter** stands for the type of Fill: **A** - White Fill; **B** - Shaded Fill.
The **second letter** stands for each Shape: **R** - Triangle; **S** - Arrow; **T** - Circle.
The answer is **BR**: B for Shaded Fill; **R** for Triangle.

Now do the questions below. Circle the correct answer.

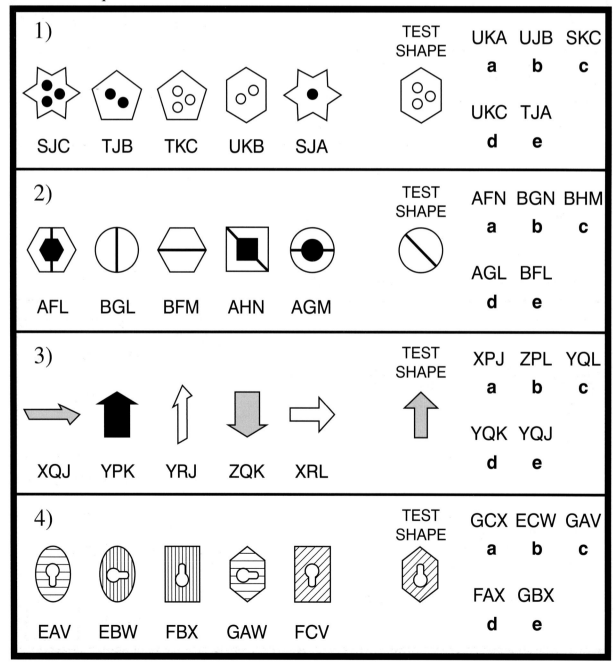

1) SJC   TJB   TKC   UKB   SJA

TEST SHAPE

UKA UJB SKC
a   b   c

UKC TJA
d   e

2) AFL   BGL   BFM   AHN   AGM

TEST SHAPE

AFN BGN BHM
a   b   c

AGL BFL
d   e

3) XQJ   YPK   YRJ   ZQK   XRL

TEST SHAPE

XPJ ZPL YQL
a   b   c

YQK YQJ
d   e

4) EAV   EBW   FBX   GAW   FCV

TEST SHAPE

GCX ECW GAV
a   b   c

FAX GBX
d   e

© 2010 Stephen Curran

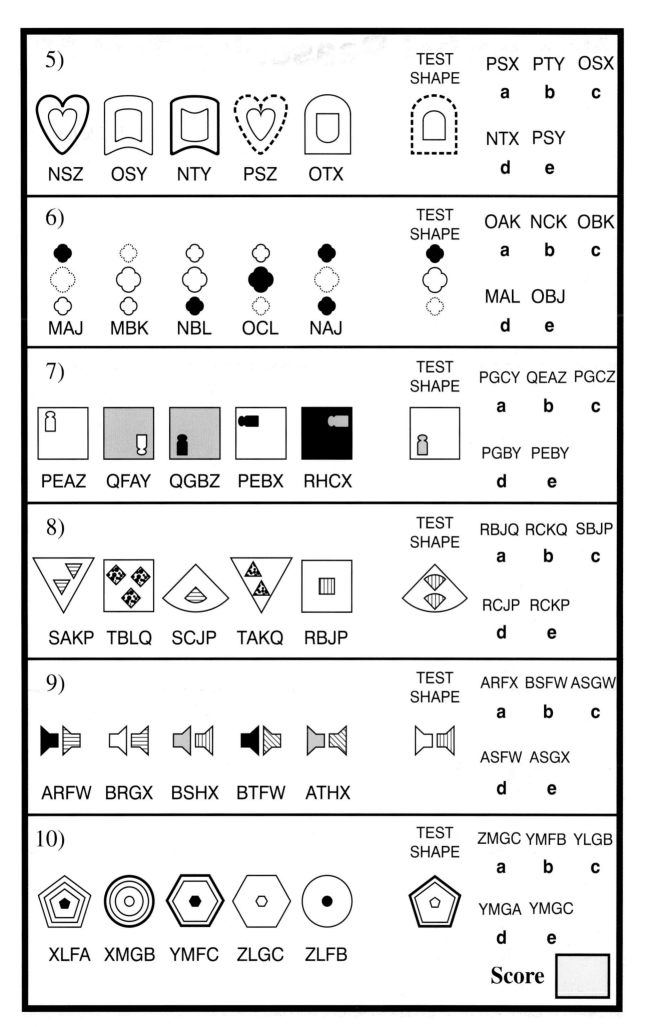

5)

NSZ OSY NTY PSZ OTX

TEST SHAPE

PSX PTY OSX
a   b   c

NTX PSY
d   e

6)

MAJ MBK NBL OCL NAJ

TEST SHAPE

OAK NCK OBK
a   b   c

MAL OBJ
d   e

7)

PEAZ QFAY QGBZ PEBX RHCX

TEST SHAPE

PGCY QEAZ PGCZ
a   b   c

PGBY PEBY
d   e

8)

SAKP TBLQ SCJP TAKQ RBJP

TEST SHAPE

RBJQ RCKQ SBJP
a   b   c

RCJP RCKP
d   e

9)

ARFW BRGX BSHX BTFW ATHX

TEST SHAPE

ARFX BSFW ASGW
a   b   c

ASFW ASGX
d   e

10)

XLFA XMGB YMFC ZLGC ZLFB

TEST SHAPE

ZMGC YMFB YLGB
a   b   c

YMGA YMGC
d   e

Score

Non-verbal Reasoning Test 37
Analogies

On the left of each row are two Shapes with an arrow between them. Decide how the second Shape is related to the first. After these there is a third Shape, then an arrow and then five more Shapes. Decide which of the five Shapes goes with the **third** Shape to **make a pair** like the two Shapes on the left.

Example

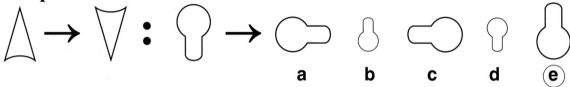

Now do the questions below. Circle the correct answer.

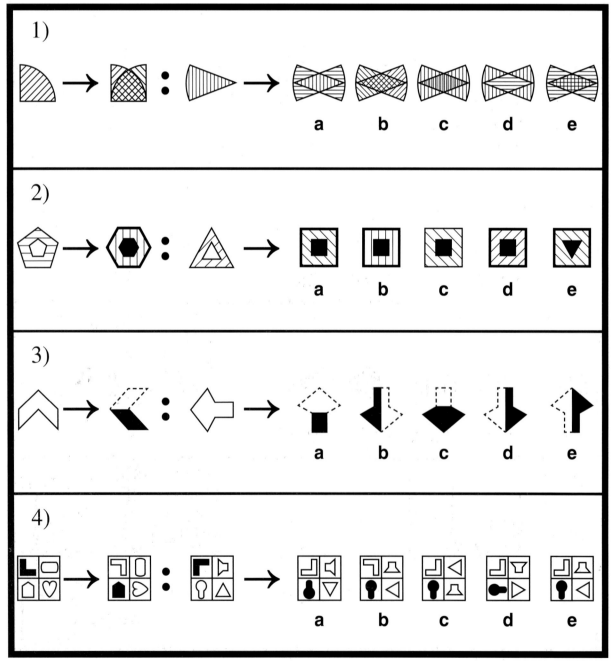

　　　　　　　　　　　© 2010 Stephen Curran ae

5)

SF → ꟻƧ : NR → ᴎᴙ ᴎᴙ RN NR ᴙᴎ

           a   b   c   d   e

6)

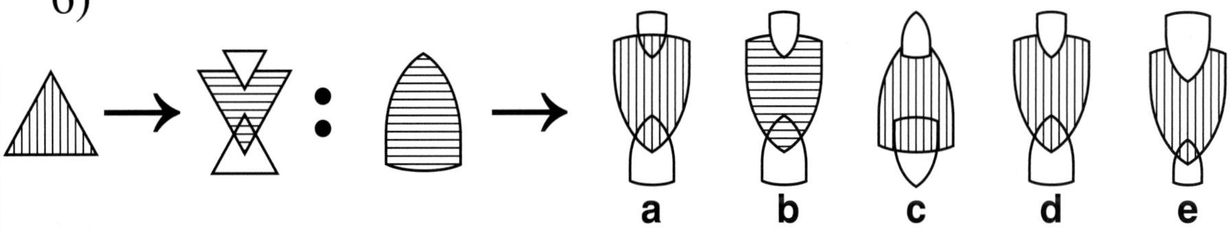

                        a   b   c   d   e

7)

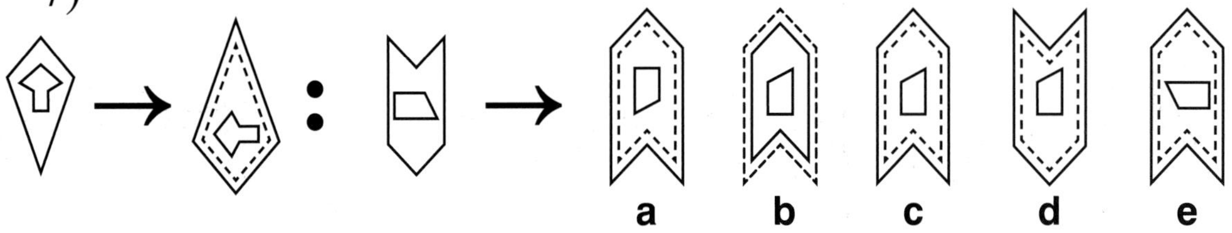

                        a   b   c   d   e

8)

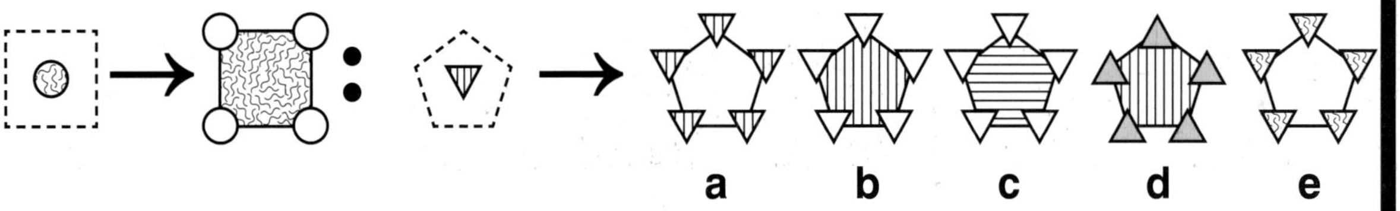

                        a   b   c   d   e

9)

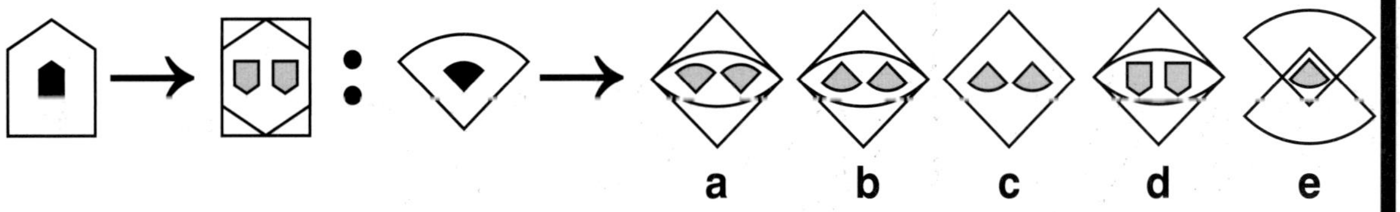

                        a   b   c   d   e

10)

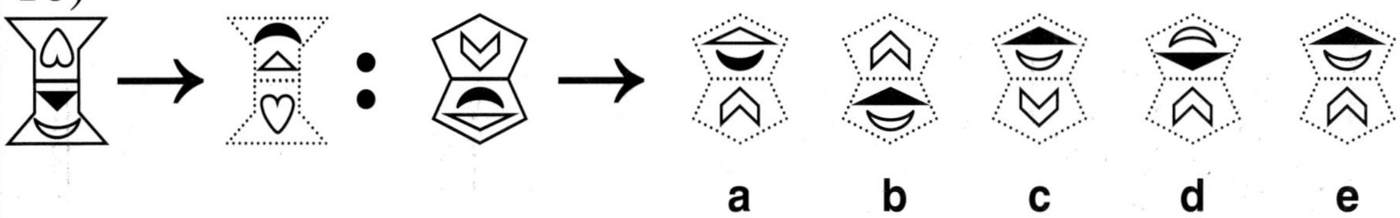

                        a   b   c   d   e

Score

ae © 2010 Stephen Curran

Non-verbal Reasoning Test 38
Similarities

On the left of each of the rows below there are two Figures that are alike. On the right there are five more Figures. Find which one of these five is **most like** the two Figures on the left.

Example

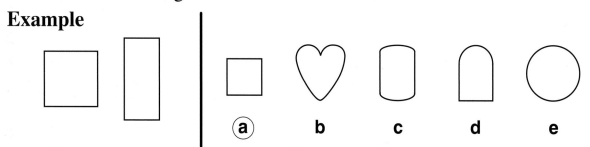

Now do the questions below. Circle the correct answer.

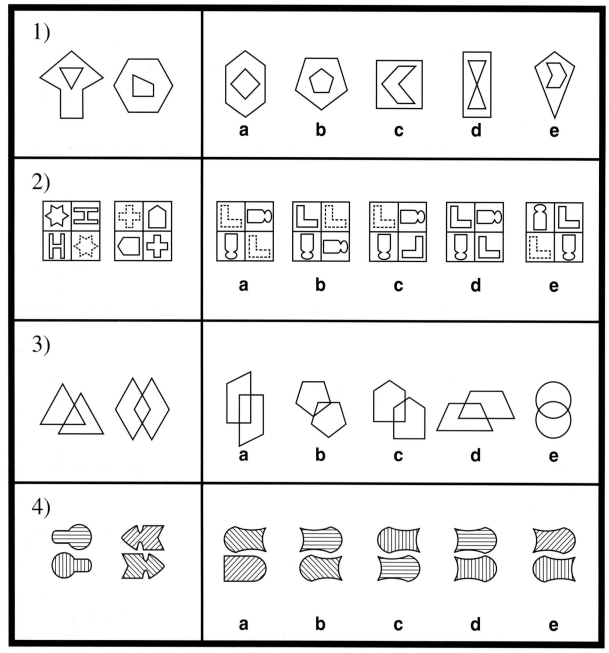

© 2010 Stephen Curran

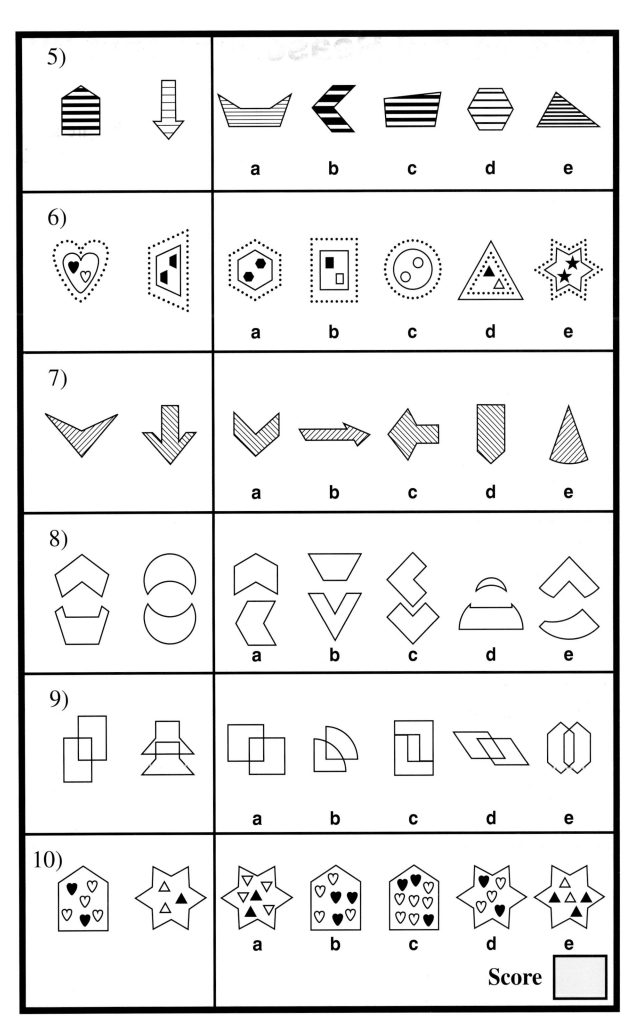

5)

a   b   c   d   e

6)

a   b   c   d   e

7)

a   b   c   d   e

8)

a   b   c   d   e

9)

a   b   c   d   e

10)

a   b   c   d   e

Score

ae © 2010 Stephen Curran

Non-verbal Reasoning Test 39
Series

To the left of each of the lines below there are five squares arranged in order. One of these squares has been left empty. Find which one of the five squares on the right should take the place of the empty square.

Example

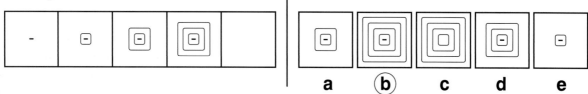

Now do the questions below. Circle the correct answer.

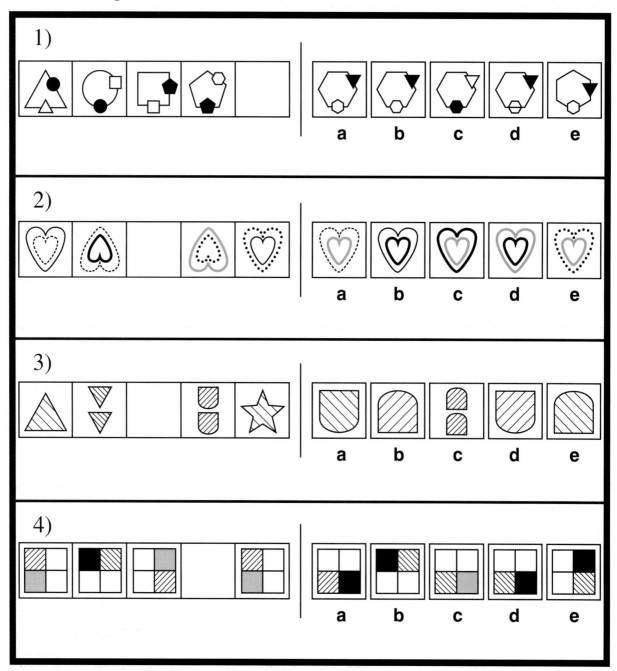

© 2010 Stephen Curran

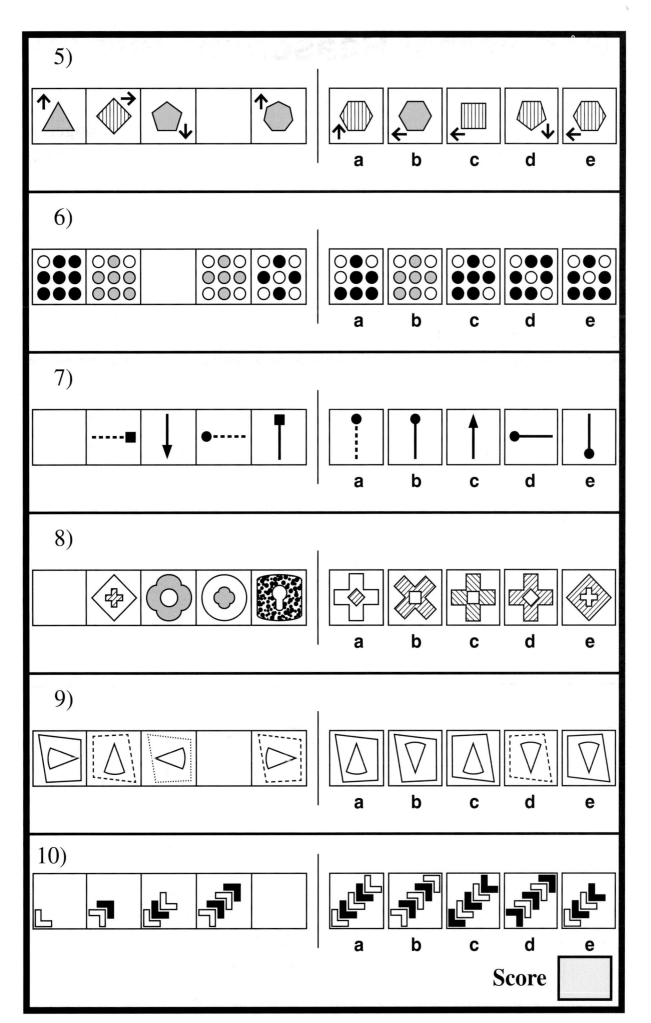

Non-verbal Reasoning Test 40
Matrices

In the big square on the left of each line below, one of the small squares has been left empty. One of the five Figures on the right should fill the empty square. Find this Figure.

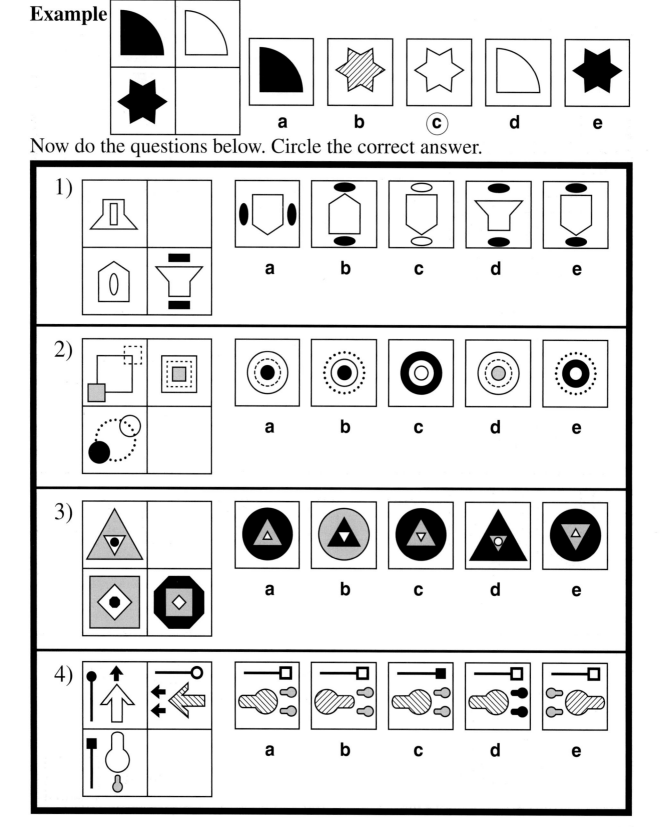

Now do the questions below. Circle the correct answer.

© 2010 Stephen Curran

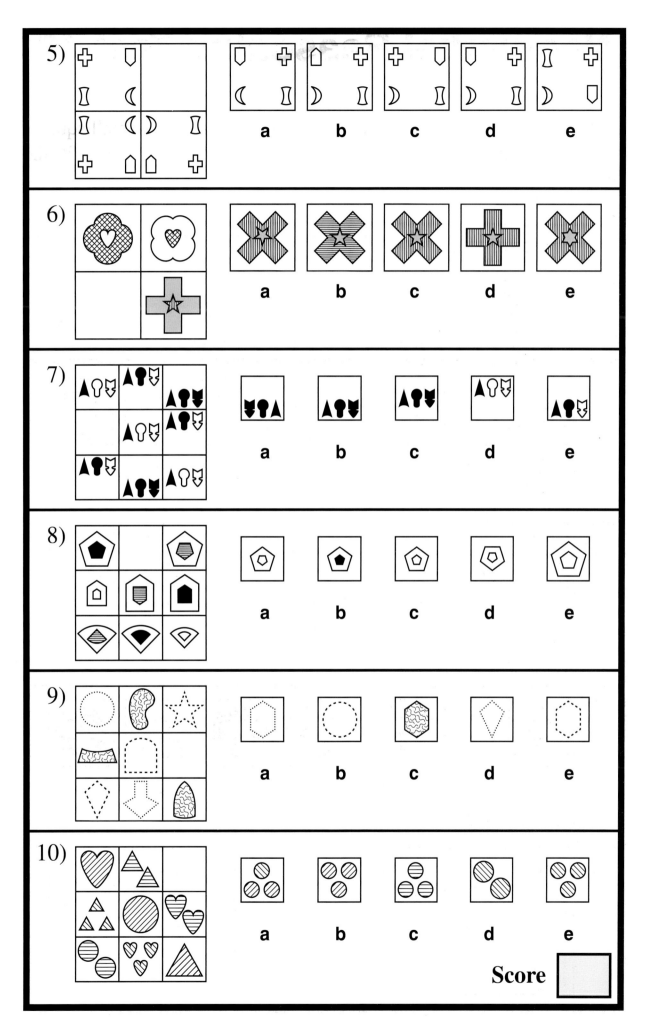

© 2010 Stephen Curran

Answers

Test 1
1) **a**
2) **c**
3) **c**
4) **b**
5) **b**
6) **e**
7) **b**
8) **d**
9) **a**
10) **c**

Test 2
1) **b**
2) **c**
3) **c**
4) **e**
5) **b**
6) **d**
7) **d**
8) **d**
9) **b**
10) **d**

Test 3
1) **b**
2) **b**
3) **d**
4) **c**
5) **d**
6) **d**
7) **c**
8) **b** and **e**
9) **c**
10) **b**

Test 4
1) **d**
2) **d**
3) **c**
4) **b**

5) **a**
6) **a**
7) **c**
8) **c** and **e**
9) **a**
10) **a**

Test 5
1) **a**
2) **d**
3) **b**
4) **c**
5) **a**
6) **d**
7) **d**
8) **b** and **c**
9) **a**
10) **d**

Test 6
1) **d**
2) **b**
3) **d**
4) **c**
5) **c**
6) **a**
7) **b**
8) **b**
9) **c**
10) **c**

Test 7
1) **a**
2) **c**
3) **b**
4) **a**
5) **b**
6) **b**
7) **b**
8) **c**
9) **c**
10) **b**

Test 8
1) **a**
2) **a**
3) **d**
4) **c**
5) **d**
6) **d**
7) **b**
8) **a** and **c**
9) **a**
10) **b**

Test 9
1) **c**
2) **c**
3) **a**
4) **b**
5) **a**
6) **b**
7) **c**
8) **b**
9) **a**
10) **e**

Test 10
1) **a**
2) **d**
3) **a**
4) **c**
5) **a**
6) **c**
7) **b**
8) **d**
9) **a** and **d**
10) **c**

Test 11
1) **d**
2) **b**
3) **d**
4) **e**

© 2010 Stephen Curran

Answers

5) **a**
6) **d**
7) **a**
8) **b**
9) **a**
10) **b**

Test 12
1) **b**
2) **b**
3) **b**
4) **a**
5) **c**
6) **d**
7) **b**
8) **b** and **c**
9) **b**
10) **b**

Test 13
1) **c**
2) **d**
3) **c**
4) **b**
5) **a**
6) **d**
7) **c**
8) **b**
9) **b**
10) **d**

Test 14
1) **b**
2) **e**
3) **c**
4) **b**
5) **d**
6) **c**
7) **b**
8) **c**
9) **b**
10) **b**

Test 15
1) **d**
2) **d**
3) **b**
4) **b**
5) **b**
6) **c**
7) **c**
8) **a**
9) **b**
10) **c**

Test 16
1) **c**
2) **a**
3) **b**
4) **c**
5) **b**
6) **c**
7) **b**
8) **a**
9) **b**
10) **c**

Test 17
1) **e**
2) **b**
3) **c**
4) **b**
5) **b**
6) **d**
7) **d**
8) **c**
9) **e**
10) **a**

Test 18
1) **d**
2) **a**
3) **b**
4) **e**
5) **c**

6) **b**
7) **d**
8) **a**
9) **c**
10) **e**

Test 19
1) **b**
2) **d**
3) **a**
4) **c**
5) **b**
6) **d**
7) **b**
8) **c**
9) **c**
10) **b**

Test 20
1) **d**
2) **d**
3) **e**
4) **c**
5) **c**
6) **e**
7) **b**
8) **a**
9) **e**
10) **b**

Test 21
1) **d**
2) **a**
3) **b**
4) **a**
5) **e**
6) **c**
7) **b**
8) **d**
9) **c**
10) **a**

© 2010 Stephen Curran

Answers

NVR Testbook 1

Test 22
1) e
2) c
3) b
4) a
5) d
6) b
7) e
8) c
9) d
10) a

Test 23
1) e
2) a
3) d
4) c
5) b
6) e
7) c
8) a
9) c
10) d

Test 24
1) c
2) b
3) e
4) b
5) e
6) d
7) a
8) c
9) d
10) e

Test 25
1) b
2) c
3) d

4) e
5) e
6) b
7) e
8) c
9) d
10) a

Test 26
1) c
2) d
3) c
4) e
5) e
6) d
7) c
8) b
9) e
10) e

Test 27
1) e
2) d
3) a
4) c
5) b
6) d
7) c
8) a
9) a
10) e

Test 28
1) c
2) a
3) c
4) b
5) a
6) e
7) c

8) c
9) e
10) b

Test 29
1) e
2) c
3) b
4) d
5) e
6) b
7) c
8) d
9) b
10) a

Test 30
1) d
2) b
3) c
4) a
5) a
6) e
7) c
8) d
9) e
10) d

Test 31
1) b
2) d
3) a
4) c
5) e
6) e
7) b
8) c
9) d
10) a

© 2010 Stephen Curran

Answers

Test 32
1) c
2) c
3) b
4) a
5) e
6) e
7) c
8) c
9) b
10) c

Test 33
1) c
2) a
3) b
4) a
5) e
6) d
7) c
8) a
9) b
10) e

Test 34
1) e
2) d
3) a
4) c
5) d
6) a
7) b
8) b
9) d
10) c

Test 35
1) d
2) b
3) e
4) a
5) c
6) c
7) a
8) b
9) e
10) c

Test 36
1) d
2) b
3) c
4) a
5) a
6) e
7) c
8) b
9) e
10) d

Test 37
1) c
2) a
3) d
4) e
5) a
6) d
7) c
8) b
9) b
10) e

Test 38
1) a
2) c
3) d
4) c
5) e
6) b
7) a
8) b
9) a
10) c

Test 39
1) b
2) c
3) b
4) d
5) e
6) c
7) b
8) d
9) e
10) a

Test 40
1) e
2) b
3) c
4) a
5) d
6) c
7) b
8) c
9) a
10) e

© 2010 Stephen Curran

PROGRESS CHARTS

Test	Mark	%
1	10/10	100
2	6/10	60
3	8/10	80
4	8/10	80
5	7/10	70
6	9/10	90
7	8/10	80
8	9/10	90
9	8/10	80
10	9/10	90
11	8/10	80
12	6/10	60
13	7/10	70
14	9/10	90
15	9/10	90
16		
17		
18		
19		
20		

Test	Mark	%
21		
22		
23		
24		
25		
26		
27		
28		
29		
30		
31		
32		
33		
34		
35		
36		
37		
38		
39		
40		

ae © 2010 Stephen Curran

CERTIFICATE
OF
ACHIEVEMENT
(First)

This certifies..................................

has completed **Non-verbal Reasoning Testbook One** successfully.

Overall Percentage
Score Achieved

%

Comment......................................

....

Signed ....
(Teacher/parent/guardian)

Date ....

© 2010 Stephen Curran ae